Traffic Signs Manual

Chapter 7

The Design of Traffic Signs

Department for Transport

Department for Regional Development (Northern Ireland)

Scottish Executive

Welsh Assembly Government

London: TSO

Traffic Signs Manual 2003

Contents of Chapters 1-8

* To be published

Published for the Department for Transport under licence from the
Controller of Her Majesty's Stationery Office

© Crown copyright 2003

Copyright in the typographical arrangements rests with the Crown.

This publication, (excluding logos) may be reproduced free of charge in any format or medium for research, private study or for internal circulation within an organisation. This is subject to it being reproduced accurately and not used in a misleading context. The material must be acknowledged as Crown copyright and the title of the publication specified.

For any other use of this material, please write to The HMSO Licensing Division, HMSO, St Clements House, 2-16 Colegate, Norwich NR3 1BQ.
Fax: 01603 72300 or e-mail: hmsolicensing@cabinet-office.x.gsi.gov.uk

ISBN 0 11 552480 0

Printed in Great Britain using material containing 55% post-consumer waste, 20% post industrial waste and 25% ECF pulp.

Chapter 7

CONTENTS

1 INTRODUCTION

GENERAL

1.1 This chapter of the Traffic Signs Manual describes how sign faces are designed. It does not include the various methods by which signs are constructed and mounted. It supersedes Local Transport Note 2/94: Directional Informatory Signs Interim Design Notes, which was withdrawn in 1997.

1.2 Reference should be made to the appropriate chapter for the use, size and siting of signs (e.g. Chapter 4 for warning signs). The basic sign face layout, including the choice of destinations, for directional signs will be included in the new Chapter 2 when this is published. During the interim period reference should be made to Local Transport Note 1/94: The Design and Use of Directional Informatory Signs, published by the Stationery Office.

1.3 Any reference to "the Regulations" or "the Directions" is a reference to the Traffic Signs Regulations and General Directions 2002 and applicable to England, Scotland and Wales. Reference to a "diagram number" is a reference to a diagram in those Regulations. In Northern Ireland the appropriate legislation is the Traffic Signs Regulations (Northern Ireland).

1.4 The Traffic Signs Manual is applicable in England, Northern Ireland, Scotland and Wales. References to "the Secretary of State" should therefore be interpreted as referring to the Secretary of State for Transport, the Department for Regional Development (Northern Ireland), the Scottish Executive or the Welsh Assembly Government as appropriate.

1.5 The design rules contained in this chapter apply to new and replacement signs erected on all types of public highway. Where signs are to be provided in accordance with the current Traffic Signs (Welsh and English Language Provisions) Regulations and General Directions, further guidance on the design of the sign faces should be sought from the Welsh Assembly Government.

WORKING DRAWINGS

1.6 Appendix A lists those signs prescribed by the Regulations for which working drawings are available either from the Stationery Office or on the Department's website. The drawings cover signs which are generally of a fixed design such as triangular warning signs. Certain other signs which have special design rules are also included in the series of working drawings. Before designing a sign, reference should therefore be made to Appendix A.

1.7 This chapter deals with those signs which are designed for a specific requirement or location such as the directional informatory signs in Parts I, II and X of Schedule 7 to the Regulations. For most of these signs, working drawings have not been provided as it is not possible to include all the relevant design details associated with the permitted variants.

1.8 Section 2 of this chapter sets out the basic design rules applicable to all rectangular signs. Sections 3 to 11 deal with directional informatory signs, section 12 certain regulatory signs (mainly time plates), section 13 temporary signs for road works, and section 14 other sign design matters.

1.9 Appendix B lists those symbols which may be used on the various types of sign included in this chapter. These include both general symbols (e.g. bus, bicycle and aircraft) and those indicating specific tourist and leisure attractions. The designs for these symbols are detailed on working drawings. Further design guidance on the use of symbols is given in section 14.

1.10 Occasionally a sign that is not prescribed by the Regulations may be authorised on behalf of the Secretary of State for placing on a public highway. Where the Department produces a drawing of such a sign for authorisation purposes, the number will be prefixed "NP" ("Non-Prescribed"). Before proceeding with any new design, it should be ascertained whether a drawing is already in existence. Where a sign does not have a working drawing, the designer should follow as closely as possible the design principles set out on the working drawings and in this chapter. Some older non-prescribed drawings prefixed WBM ("Worboys series B - Metric") will continue to be used for special authorisation purposes until replaced by new drawings. Working drawings for non-prescribed general symbols and tourist attraction symbols are prefixed "NS" and "NT" respectively. All non-prescribed signs must be submitted for special authorisation.

1.11 The Regulations refer to approved tourist attraction symbols. These are shown on drawings prefixed "AT" and may be used without the need for special authorisation (see Appendix B).

2 DESIGN RULES COMMON TO ALL RECTANGULAR SIGNS

ALPHABETS

2.1 The alphanumeric characters used on traffic signs are from a specially designed alphabet known as the Transport alphabet. There are two versions: Transport Medium for white characters on a green, blue, brown, red or black background (Schedule 13 Part I in the Regulations); Transport Heavy for black characters on a white or yellow background (Schedule 13 Part II). Route numbers on green background signs are yellow and are from the Transport Medium alphabet. Some signs have an orange background and in most cases the characters are black from the Transport Heavy alphabet, but in diagrams 2714 and 2715 white Transport Medium characters are generally used. Transport Heavy characters use a slightly thicker stroke width than Transport Medium characters.

2.2 Light-coloured surfaces, especially when illuminated, irradiate into adjacent darker ones. Thus white characters on a dark background appear thicker than their actual size, whereas black characters on a light background appear thinner. The use of the medium alphabet for white and yellow legends, and the heavy alphabet for black legends compensates for this effect and ensures optimum legibility.

2.3 Most route numbers on motorway signs are from an enlarged Motorway alphabet. Again there are two versions: the standard Motorway alphabet for white characters on permanent blue background signs (Schedule 13 Part III in the Regulations); and the Motorway Black alphabet for black characters on temporary yellow background signs (Schedule 13 Part IV).

2.4 The four alphabets are shown on drawings TM 1, TM 2, TM 3 (TM being Transport Medium), TH 1, TH 2, TH 3 (TH being Transport Heavy), MW 1 (MW being Motorway White) and MB 1 (MB being Motorway Black). These are available either from the Stationery Office as part of the package of working drawings or on the Department's website.

TILES, X-HEIGHTS AND STROKE WIDTHS

2.5 To ensure correct letter spacing when forming a word, the characters in each alphabet are placed on imaginary tiles. The tiles vary in width, according to the size of the character, and have a fixed height which ensures correct line spacing. All design spaces are measured to the edge of the tiles and not to the actual characters, unless special rules state otherwise. Tile outlines must not appear on the finished sign.

2.6 The size of an alphabet is specified in terms of its *x-height*. This is the height of the lower case letter "x", and is the same for both the Transport Medium and Heavy alphabets. The unit of measurement when designing a sign is the *stroke width* (sw) which is one quarter of the x-height and is not necessarily equivalent to the width of any given character. *The dimensions shown in all figures in this chapter are given in stroke widths unless otherwise stated.*

2.7 The *tile height* for any alphabet is twice the x-height (i.e. 8 sw). Thus for an x-height of 250 mm the tile height is 500 mm. For the two motorway alphabets, where there are no lower case letters, the units of measurement are still x-heights and stroke widths. Thus if the x-height of the main sign is 300 mm the tile height for both the Transport Medium and Motorway alphabets is 600 mm.

2.8 Figure 2-1 shows how the characters from the various alphabets are placed on the tiles. It can be seen that the lower case letters without ascenders or descenders are centred vertically on the tiles, leaving an equal gap of 2 sw top and bottom. The capital letters and numerals from the Transport alphabets are 5.6 sw high, with a gap to the top of the tile of 0.4 sw. The characters in the Motorway alphabet are 8 sw high and vertically fill the tile.

WORDS AND HORIZONTAL SPACING

2.9 Words are formed by butting the letter tiles together. The tile widths, listed in Appendix C, have been designed to ensure the correct spacing of the letters. However, for certain combinations of letters the tile widths have to be adjusted and these special tile widths are also specified in Appendix C.

2.10 The spacing between two words on the same line is 2.5 sw. Some signs indicate distances (e.g. 100 yards) or time of day (e.g. 8.30 am). Where abbreviations are used for the unit of measurement the normal word spacing of 2.5 sw is reduced. Where dates are abbreviated, such as "15 Sept" or "Feb 98", the spacing remains at 2.5 sw. Figure 2-2 shows the appropriate horizontal spacing between different elements of the sign and for abbreviated legends. Where two symbols are placed side by side

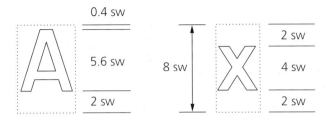

4 sw = x-height

TRANSPORT MEDIUM

Light letters on Dark backgrounds

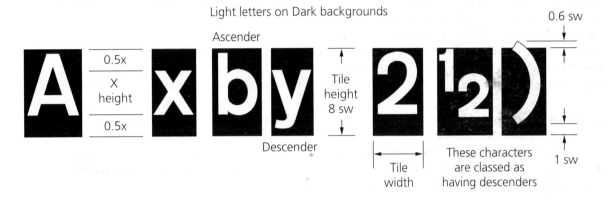

TRANSPORT HEAVY

Dark letters on Light backgrounds

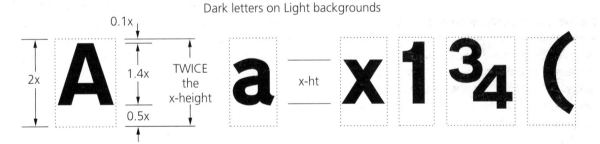

ROUTE NUMBERS USED ON MOTORWAY SIGNS

Full tile used

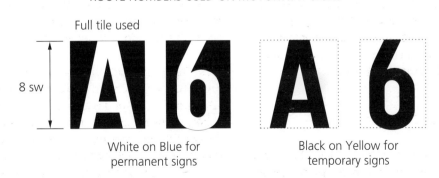

White on Blue for permanent signs   Black on Yellow for temporary signs

Figure 2-1

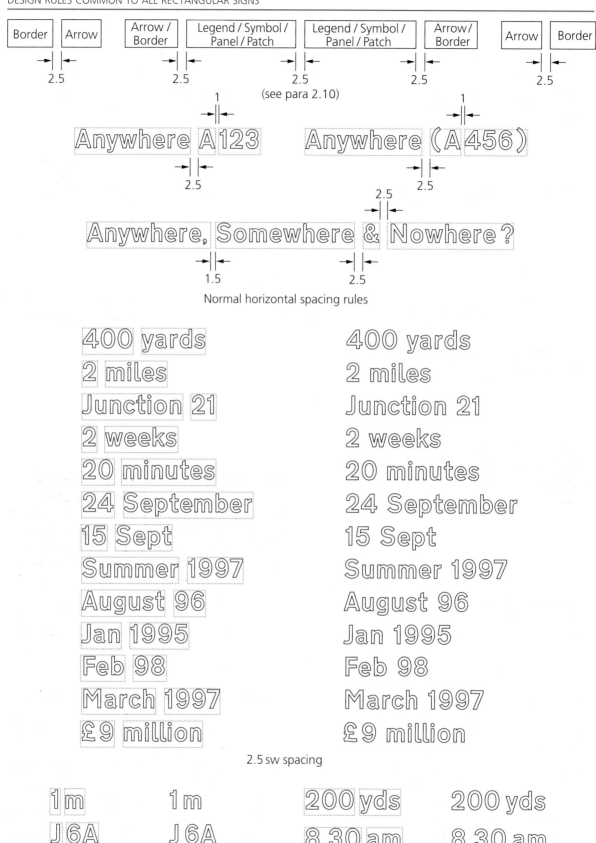

Normal horizontal spacing rules

Figure 2-2

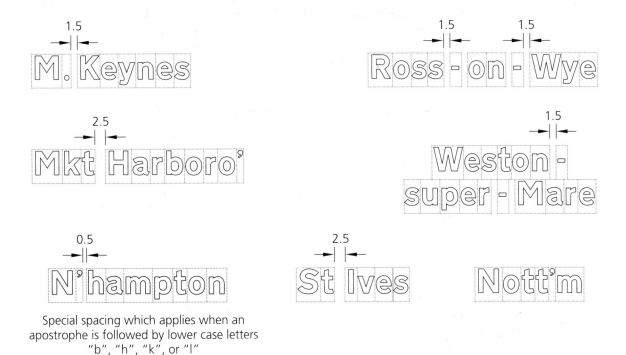

Special spacing which applies when an apostrophe is followed by lower case letters "b", "h", "k", or "l"

Figure 2-3

the horizontal spacing is generally 2.5 sw (as for words). However, for certain symbols the horizontal spacing is increased to 4 sw. Further guidance on symbol spacing is given in section 14.

ABBREVIATIONS

2.11 In some cases it may be desirable to abbreviate place names. An apostrophe is normally used to indicate where letters have been omitted. Generally, an abbreviated word should not use more than one apostrophe. Where the lower case letter "b", "h", "k" or "l" follows an apostrophe there should be a space of 0.5 sw between the apostrophe and that letter. Certain abbreviations, such as "Mkt" for "Market" do not use apostrophes. Where a word is expressed as a single letter it is followed by a full stop (this is to ensure that it is linked to the next part of the name without the two capital letters, such as M and K in M. Keynes, being too close together). Where the single letter is the last character of a name which is not followed by a route number or mileage on the same line (e.g. Stoke-on-T or Tunbridge W) the full stop can be omitted. For other abbreviations full stops are generally not used. Examples of abbreviated place names, together with appropriate horizontal spacings, are shown in figure 2-3. Certain names are hyphenated (e.g. Ross-on-Wye) and the correct horizontal spacing for these is also shown.

BASIC SIGN DESIGN

2.12 The basic unit of measurement is the stroke width (sw), which is equal to one quarter of the x-height of the letters. As a general rule, the x-height on any one sign should be the same for all legends. However, there are some designs where more than one x-height is used and in such cases the dimensions given in stroke widths will be based on the main x-height unless stated otherwise.

2.13 Dimensions are measured to the *tile outlines* and not to the actual letter. This also applies to any symbol shown with an outline tile or grid.

2.14 The simplest sign is the supplementary plate as illustrated in figure 2-4. Where the legend is on two lines, the letter tiles are butted together vertically as shown. There may be some designs where it is necessary to insert a vertical space between the tiles. Figure 2-5 illustrates diagram 502 where a 2 sw gap has been introduced between "STOP" and "100 yds". This is because the legend is considered to have two distinct messages. The first, "STOP", gives an instruction and the second "100 yds" tells the driver when to carry out that instruction. The 2 sw vertical space helps to separate the two parts of the message and make the sign easier to read. Correct vertical spacing is important; it is the sign designer's equivalent of punctuation.

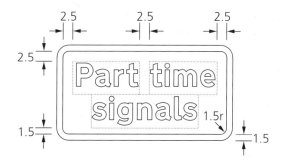

diagram 575

diagram 661.3A

Figure 2-4 (diagram 543.1)

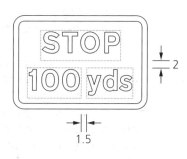

Figure 2-5 (diagram 502)

Figure 2-6

2.15 A standard border width of 1.5 sw has now been adopted for most prescribed signs (prior to the 1994 Regulations, 1 sw was used for supplementary plates). Where a different border width is used the inside corner radius of the main sign will generally be equal to that border width.

2.16 Where the legend is in lower case letters, only the first word of each message will commence with a capital letter. Capital letters are used at the beginning of each word only where the words form a proper name. Examples are shown in figure 2-6.

2.17 Figure 2-7 shows the design of diagram 865 where all letters are in block capitals. The appearance of the sign is improved by centring the legend vertically on the sign and this is achieved by adopting the dimensions shown.

2.18 Where the legend is on two or more lines each line is centred horizontally on the sign. Special rules apply to directional signs; these are covered in section 3.

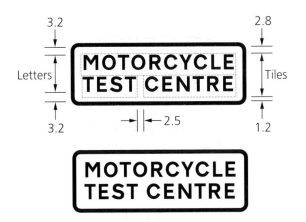

Figure 2-7 (diagram 865)

2.19 Some signs are divided into more than one panel, such as diagram 618.3 illustrated in figure 2-8. The dividing border between each panel has the same width and corner radii as the main sign border. The exception to this is the stack type direction sign which has special design rules (see section 4). The decision to provide more than one panel is based on the need to separate distinct parcels of information.

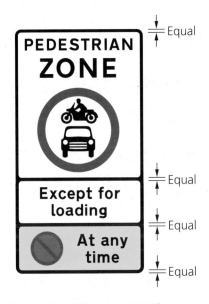

Figure 2-8 (diagram 618.3)

2.20 The overall size of a sign is determined by the chosen x-height. This will depend on the type of sign and, in most cases, the 85 percentile speed of vehicles using the road. There is a range of standard x-heights from 15 mm (for some waiting restriction time plates not intended to be read from moving vehicles) to 400 mm (for motorway signs). Some signs have specific x-heights prescribed by the Regulations. However, many signs, particularly directional informatory signs, have only minimum and maximum

sizes given. In theory any intermediate value could be used, but it is recommended that the main x-height should be to the nearest 5 mm. The table of x-heights for directional signs in Appendix A of Local Transport Note 1/94 lists the standard sizes of 50, 60, 75, 100, 125, 150, 200, 250, 300 and 400 mm. Intermediate x-heights may be used where this would have siting advantages (e.g. spanning a footway) without compromising the target value and legibility of the sign.

ROUNDING OF SIGN SIZES

2.21 With the use of computers in the design and manufacture of traffic sign faces it is not always necessary to round the overall size of a particular sign to "convenient" dimensions. However, where it is considered advantageous to round the size of a sign the following guidelines should be used.

2.22 The amount of rounding is based on the main x-height of the sign. The overall size of the sign shall be rounded up to the nearest Z mm where Z is calculated by taking 5% of the x-height and then rounding up to the nearest 5 mm. Thus for a sign with 150 mm x-height, Z would equal 5% of 150 mm which is 7.5 mm and this would be rounded up to 10 mm. The overall size of the sign, in this case, would be rounded up to the nearest 10 mm. The table in figure 2-9 gives the value of Z for each standard x-height.

x-height mm	<100	100	125	150	200	250	300	400
Z mm	5	5	10	10	10	15	15	20

Figure 2-9 : Rounding of Sign Sizes

2.23 The rounding described in para 2.22 is applied by increasing the space between the sign border and the elements that make up the sign by equal amounts top and bottom, and both sides. Where a sign comprises more than one panel (see para 2.19) the rounding of the vertical dimension may be split equally between each panel or applied to the top and bottom borders only, as for other signs.

2.24 In some cases it may be desirable to round either the vertical or horizontal overall dimension by varying the x-height (see variable x-heights in para 2.20). This method would be appropriate where the sign is being manufactured by computer methods.

TYPES OF DIRECTIONAL SIGNS

3.1 Directional informatory signs can be categorised as follows:

(a) Advance Direction Signs - those signs giving route information in respect of a junction ahead.

(b) Direction Signs - those signs placed *at* a junction and pointing along specific routes.

(c) Route Confirmatory Signs - those signs placed after a junction giving confirmation as to the route being followed and, in most cases, destinations that can be reached, together with the appropriate distances.

3.2 Advance direction signs can be either post mounted or gantry mounted. They are sited on the approach to the junctions indicated to give drivers adequate advance warning. There are three types of post mounted signs: map type, stack type and dedicated lane signs. An example of each is illustrated in figure 3-1. Gantry mounted signs are generally used for grade separated junctions. There are two distinctive designs; one for junctions without lane drops and one for junctions with lane drops. *It is vitally important that the correct design is used for the two different types of junction*. An example of each design is illustrated in figure 3-2.

Map-type Sign

Stack-type Sign

Dedicated Lane Sign

Figure 3-1

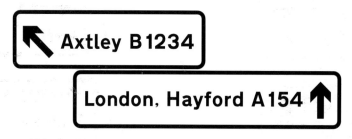

Advance Direction Sign for Junction without Lane Drop

Advance Direction Sign for Junction with Lane Drop
(also used as a Route Confirmatory Sign)

Figure 3-2

3.3 Direction signs must not be confused with advance direction signs. *Direction signs are placed at the junction and point along the route shown on the sign.* The most common type of direction

Figure 3-3

sign is the flag type sign with the chevron end. An example is illustrated in figure 3-3. Where the exit from a junction is at an acute angle, a flag type sign may not be suitable. In such cases a rectangular sign with an inclined arrow may be used. This should not be confused with the stack type advance direction sign which it resembles. One common use of the rectangular sign is on the nose of an exit slip road at a grade separated junction. Examples of rectangular direction signs are illustrated in figure 3-4. A third type of direction sign is the modern version of the traditional fingerpost (diagram 2141). This should be used only on minor rural roads where traffic speeds are low. The Directions do not permit this type of

sign, an example of which is illustrated in figure 3-5, to be erected on trunk, principal ("A" numbered) or classified "B" numbered roads.

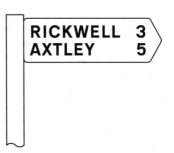

Figure 3-5

3.4 Route confirmatory signs are generally placed after junctions where the advance direction signs do not give distances to the various destinations. A route confirmatory sign will normally show the route number, destinations reached and the distances to those destinations. In some cases it is appropriate to give information relating to another route that can be reached at a junction ahead. At grade separated junctions with gantry mounted signs, overhead signs may be provided beyond the nose of the exit slip road. Although they will not include distances, they are referred to as route confirmatory signs (see figure 3-2). Examples of the various types of post mounted route confirmatory signs are illustrated in figure 3-6.

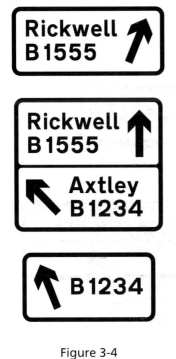

Figure 3-4

Figure 3-6

BASIC PRINCIPLES OF COLOUR CODING

3.5 Colour coding is one of the most important aspects of directional sign design. Since 1964 blue backgrounds have been used on motorway signs, green backgrounds on primary routes and white backgrounds on other roads (non-primary routes). The Traffic Signs Regulations and General Directions 1994 extended this colour coding to panels and patches which indicate the *status of routes* reached directly or indirectly from a junction ahead.

3.6 The layout in figure 3-7 shows a typical highway network comprising primary and non-primary routes. The signing of the network using the colour coding rules is illustrated by the five advance direction signs (labelled A to E inclusive).

3.7 Sign A is placed on the *primary* route and therefore has a *green* background with a white border. Although Longchurch is reached by travelling along a *non-primary* route (B1144), it is shown directly on the *green* background of sign A. This is because at this location the route to Longchurch continues along the primary route. Note that the route number (B1144) is not shown on a white patch. *Route number patches are used only to indicate routes of a higher status* (i.e. blue motorway patches on white and green background signs, and green patches on white background signs). As the A123 is a *non-primary route*, the place names and route numbers are shown on *white* panels. Had the B1255 been a primary route then the bracketed route number would be on a green patch on the white panel. *It should be noted that the white panel indicates the status of the route and not that of the destination.* Dorfield, for example, could be a primary destination.

3.8 Sign B shows the same junction as viewed from the non-primary route. The green panel indicating the primary route to Lampton also includes Longchurch. The same principle applies as for sign A. It is not appropriate to place Longchurch (B1144) on the main white background of the sign outside the green panel. There is no significance in the fact that a stack type sign is illustrated here, whereas sign A on the primary route is a map type sign. The type of sign used will be the most suitable for the approach to the junction. Note that all white background directional signs (other than MoD signs) have black borders. The use of blue borders on local signs was discontinued in 1994. Existing blue-bordered signs must be removed by 31st December 2014.

3.9 Sign C shows the sign at the previous junction on the A123. As this is a junction between two non-primary routes the use of green panels is not appropriate. However the sign does indicate that the primary route A11 can be reached at a junction further ahead and therefore the route number is shown on a green patch. This is similar to the current practice of signing routes to motorways by using blue motorway number patches. Had the A123 been a primary route from its junction with the A11 to Hopford then the route number A123 (unbracketed) would also be shown on a green patch. Longchurch is not indicated at this junction, but if it were the route number would not be on a green patch since the B1144 is not a primary route (see Dorfield on sign E). Green patches are used only to indicate those routes that have primary status. Although the B1144 is reached by travelling along the primary route (A11), it is itself a non-primary route and therefore a green patch is not appropriate.

3.10 Sign D shows that some situations can arise where all destinations are shown on panels. In the same way that Longchurch is shown on a green panel on sign B, Dorfield is also shown on a green panel although the A123 is a non-primary route. A green panel shows all destinations that can be reached by turning directly onto a primary route. As explained in para 3.7, white patches are not used and therefore it is not appropriate to use white patches on green panels.

3.11 Sign E indicating a junction between two non-primary routes demonstrates that other non-primary routes ahead (in this case A123) do not have their route numbers on green patches even though they are reached by travelling along a length of primary route. Sign E also demonstrates the use of a route number (B1144) not directly associated with a place name.

3.12 The background colour of direction signs (e.g. flag type signs) at a junction will be appropriate to the route indicated. Green or white panels are not used except where two directions are indicated on rectangular signs at junctions (see diagram 2127). Route number patches are used in the same manner as on advance direction signs. Where a rectangular direction sign, showing a route number only, is used to indicate an exit slip road leading directly to a non-primary route from a primary route, *the background colour should be white*, not green with a white route number panel or patch.

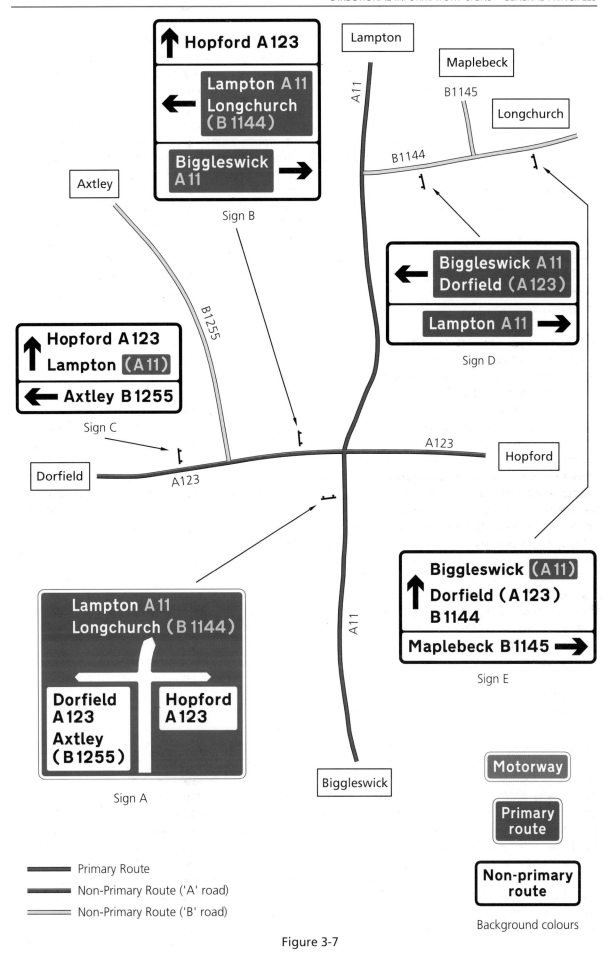

Figure 3-7

3.13 Local Transport Note 1/94: The Design and Use of Directional Informatory Signs (to be superseded by Chapter 2) gives more detailed information on the principles of directional signing (see para 1.2).

DESIGN OF PANELS AND PATCHES

3.14 Panels are designed in a similar manner to the basic sign described in section 2 in that the space between tiles and the inside border or edge is the same. Borders, which are always white, are used when a dark coloured panel is placed on a dark coloured background (e.g. a blue motorway panel on a green primary route sign). Where a border is applied this will be 0.5 sw wide with an internal corner radius of 1 sw (note that the radius is *not* equal to the border width). When a border is not required the corner radius of the panel is 1 sw. *Panels are not placed on other panels* (e.g. a brown tourist panel is not placed on a green or white destination panel). Two separate panels would be placed one above the other.

3.15 The Ministry of Defence (MoD) panel differs from the others as it has a 1 sw border which is coloured red. This border is always applied to the panel, which has a white background. When the panel is placed on a dark background, a 0.5 sw white edge (equivalent to the border on other panels) is added to the outside of the red border.

3.16 On map type signs it is sometimes possible to tuck the route symbol into the legend block, in order to reduce the overall size of the sign. This can be accommodated by providing a cut-out in one of the corners of the panel. When a cut-out is provided this should be sufficient to accommodate the route symbol. It should not be extended to provide the minimum 2.5 sw horizontal gap to the letter tiles of the lower line, unless this is necessary to provide space for the route symbol. In most cases the cut-out will be in the bottom right hand corner, as shown in figure 3-8 (see also para 5.11).

3.17 Patches are similar to panels but have reduced space between the tiles and the inside border or edge. The corner radii remain the same as for panels. A patch may contain more than one route number on the same line. A second line should not be used and therefore it is not appropriate to provide a cut-out as for panels. A white border is provided when a dark coloured patch is placed on a dark coloured background. Patches may be placed on panels.

3.18 Figure 3-8 shows in detail the design of patches and panels.

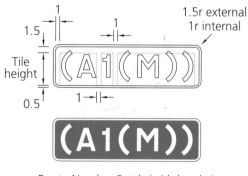

Route Number Patch (with border)

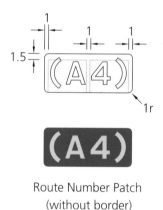

Route Number Patch
(without border)

Figure 3-8

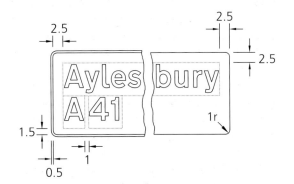

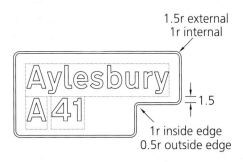

All Panels other than MoD
(with and without border)

Bordered Panel with Cut-out

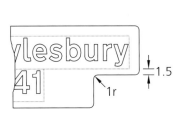

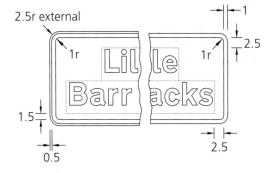

Borderless Panel with Cut-out

MoD Panel (main border red)
(with and without white edge)

Figure 3-8 (continued)

VERTICAL POSITIONING OF SYMBOLS AND PATCHES ALONGSIDE TILES

3.19 The general rule, as illustrated in figure 3-9, is that a symbol is centred vertically alongside the tiles of a legend and then moved upwards by 0.5 sw. On a simple sign this has the effect of centring the symbol vertically between the top and bottom borders whilst maintaining the correct vertical spacing for the legend tiles. The minimum vertical space between the symbol and the sign borders is 2.5 sw. On signs where close proximity to a border may not be a consideration, this rule has the effect of producing a more balanced appearance by taking account of the space on the tiles beneath the baseline of the letters.

3.20 When a patched route number is placed alongside a single line legend the rule given in para 3.19 does not apply. The tiles of both the place name and route number must align vertically. If the legend block is adjacent to both the top and bottom border of a sign or edge of a panel, then the patch will be centred on the sign or panel with a minimum vertical gap of 2.5 sw. An example is shown in figure 3-10. When a patched route number is placed alongside a two line legend it is treated the same as a symbol in terms of vertical alignment. An example is shown in figure 3-11.

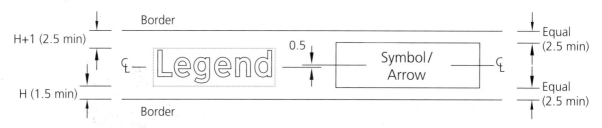

GENERAL RULE FOR PLACING SYMBOL/ARROW ALONGSIDE TILES

SINGLE LINE LEGEND
(symbol positioned as above)

TWO LINE LEGEND
(symbol positioned as above)

Figure 3-9

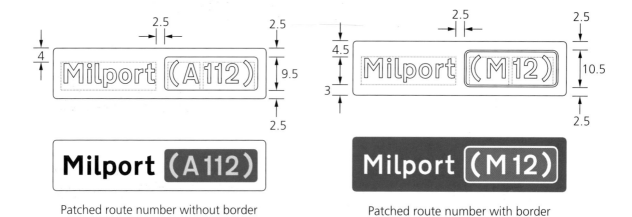

Patched route number without border

Patched route number with border

Figure 3-10

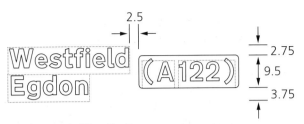

Figure 3-11

MORE THAN ONE ROUTE NUMBER ON THE SAME LINE

3.21 Figure 3-12 shows the most likely combinations of route numbers on the same line. It is not permissible to place a patched route number inside brackets with other unpatched route numbers.

The correct and incorrect ways of dealing with this situation are shown in figure 3-13.

DESTINATION BLOCKS

3.22 A place name and its associated route number (if any) is referred to as a block. A block can be a single line legend with the route number to the right of the place name. Alternatively, the route number may be positioned below the place name and ranged left. For certain sign designs the route number may be ranged right and details of this are covered in the relevant sections below (see also diagrams 2009, 2017, 2112, 2115, 2121 and 2127 in the Regulations). Two or more place names may be associated with the same route number. The route number may be placed alongside the place names to the right and positioned vertically as described

Figure 3-12

Incorrect

Correct

(A220 A24)

(A220) (A24)

(A220 (M24))

(A220) (M24)

Figure 3-13

below, but *where the names occupy three or more lines the route number should always be positioned below the names and ranged left or right as appropriate*. A single name such as "Market Harborough" may be on two lines which are centred horizontally. Other destinations in the block will be ranged left with the longest line (i.e. "Harborough" in the example given). A block may contain a patched route number and/or a symbol. Where a block has more than one line of legend the vertical space between each line is known as "*line spacing*". Figure 3-14 shows the various combinations of line spacing, together with examples.

3.23 Where a non-patched bracketed route number is placed below the legend, line spacing is always 0.5 sw whether the legend has a descender or not.

3.24 Where a patch or symbol is placed below a tiled legend, line spacing is increased to 1 sw when the legend has a descender. However, where the descender tile is to the left or right of the patch or symbol by a horizontal distance not less than 2.5 sw, the standard vertical gap of 0.5 sw can be used. For a patch this horizontal distance of 2.5 sw is measured from the outside vertical face, ignoring the radius on the corners. In the case of a symbol, judgement will be required in ascertaining the point from where the measurement is made (this may not necessarily be the edge of the symbol tile).

3.25 More than one destination block may be associated with the same route. The additional blocks will generally have different route numbers which will be bracketed. Facilities such as railway stations, hospitals, council offices etc. should be grouped together as a separate block and should not form part of the destination/route number block. There may also be instances where a village on a main route is not included with the primary destination and is shown below the route number. Again this forms a separate block. Tourist attraction, MoD, lorry

route and parking place panels also are treated as separate blocks. All blocks associated with the same routes are grouped together and ranged left with a vertical gap between each block. This gap is known as "*block spacing*". Figure 3-15 shows the various combinations of block spacing, together with examples. Block spacing for destinations associated with different routes on map type signs is dealt with in paras 5.14 to 5.17.

3.26 Where a patch or panel has a border the vertical gaps for both line and block spacing are measured to the outside edge of that border.

3.27 Where a line of legend has a patched route number which does not overlap any tiled legend above or below, it may be possible to use the appropriate line or block spacing for the adjacent tiled legends. There should be a horizontal space of at least 6 sw between the beginning of the left hand edge of the patch and the end of the line above or below. Examples are shown in figure 3-16.

3.28 Where a single block contains more than one destination and at least one of the destinations is on two lines, a vertical gap, similar to block spacing, is introduced between each destination to avoid any confusion. An example is illustrated in figure 3-17.

3.29 An aircraft symbol denoting an airport may be positioned alongside a place name. The same vertical positioning rules apply as for other symbols. As this symbol is likely to appear in a list of place names forming a destination block, line spacing for the individual place names and route number is adjusted, as shown in figure 3-18.

3.30 Where a sign contains several blocks associated with the same route, the clarity of the sign may be improved by increasing the block spacing by 2 sw. This is particularly applicable to tourist attraction signs where long names might lead to sign overload. An example is shown in figure 3-19.

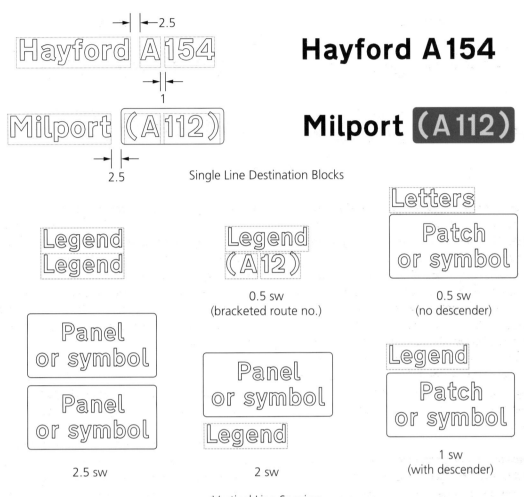

Single Line Destination Blocks

0.5 sw
(bracketed route no.)

0.5 sw
(no descender)

2.5 sw

2 sw

1 sw
(with descender)

Vertical Line Spacing

Examples of Line Spacing

Figure 3-14

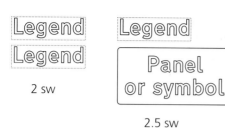

Vertical Block Spacing

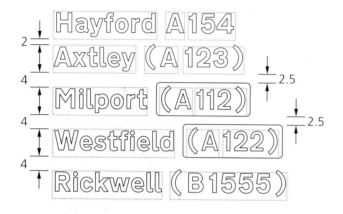

Examples of Block Spacing

Figure 3-15

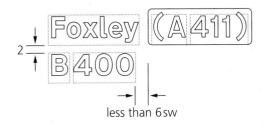

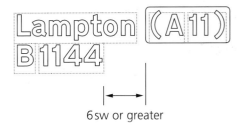

less than 6 sw

6 sw or greater

Foxley (A 411)
B 400

Line spacing measured from patch to
legend below (see figure 3-14)

Lampton (A 11)
B 1144

Line spacing measured from legend to
legend below (see figure 3-14)

Figure 3-16

Block with name on
two lines - normal line
spacing (not appropriate
in this case)

Lutterworth
Market
Harborough
A 427

"Lutterworth Market" or "Market Harborough"?

Special line spacing
(applies where the block
contains at least two place
names and one name is
on two lines)

Lutterworth
Market
Harborough
A 427

"Lutterworth" and "Market Harborough"

Figure 3-17

Equal (2 sw)

Equal (2 sw)

0.5

10

Camchester
Stansford
A 122

Figure 3-18

BLOCK SPACING = 2 sw
(normal spacing)

BLOCK SPACING = 4 sw

Figure 3-19

TWO OR MORE DESTINATIONS WITH SYMBOLS TO THE LEFT OF THE LEGEND

3.31 Where two or more destinations each contain a symbol to the left of the place name or facility, the appearance of the sign can be improved by centring the symbols above each other and ranging the tiled destinations to the left. An example is shown in figure 3-20.

Normal horizontal spacing rules

Preferred design

Figure 3-20

DISTANCES

3.32 A destination (including any symbol to the right of the place name) may be followed by the appropriate mileage on the same line. The minimum horizontal gap is 7 sw measured between the distance and the place name on the same line, on the line immediately above or on the line immediately below. This is illustrated in figure 3-21. For the design

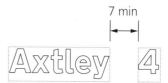

Minimum horizontal gap to distance
on same line as place name

Axtley   4

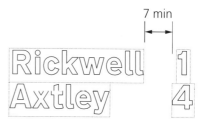

Minimum horizontal gap to "4"
measured to place name on line above

Rickwell   1
Axtley   4

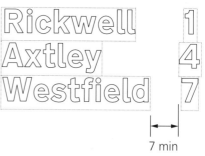

Minimum horizontal gap to "4"
measured to place name on line below

Rickwell   1
Axtley   4
Westfield   7

Figure 3-21

of certain signs where distances are expressed as "x miles", "x yards" or "x yds" see para 14.3.

3.33 Where distances are shown on successive lines they are arranged to form columns, as shown in figure 3-22. The tens and units columns are aligned horizontally so that no tiles on the same line overlap. Where there are three numerals (e.g. 101) the columns shall be equally spaced as far as possible. Where a distance is less than 1 mile and the distance immediately below does not include a fraction, special rules are used, as shown in figure 3-23.

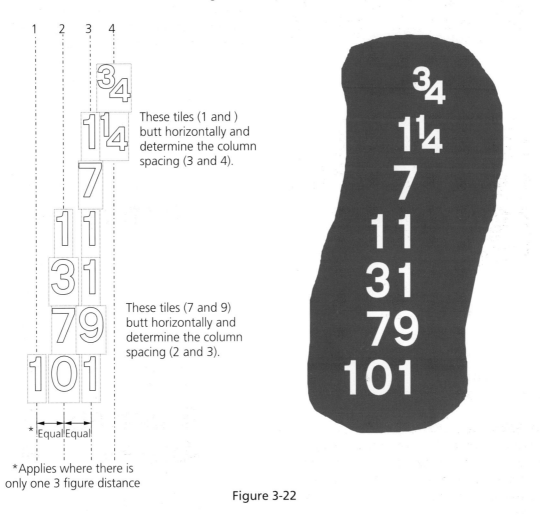

These tiles (1 and) butt horizontally and determine the column spacing (3 and 4).

These tiles (7 and 9) butt horizontally and determine the column spacing (2 and 3).

*Applies where there is only one 3 figure distance

Figure 3-22

Distance less than 1 mile directly above distance without fraction (no other fractions on sign)

Distance less than 1 mile directly above distance without fraction (with another fraction on the sign)

Figure 3-23

Matwell
avoiding low bridge
B 2199

Matwell
avoiding low bridge
(A 235)

Matwell
avoiding low bridge
(A 221)

Line Spacing (normal spacing plus 0.5 sw)

Matwell
avoiding low bridge
Catling B 2199

Matwell
avoiding low bridge

Panel or patch

Block Spacing (normal spacing plus 0.5 sw)

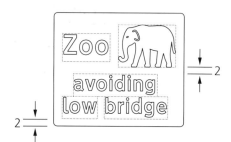

Matwell
avoiding low bridge

Panel or Sign (normal spacing plus 0.5 sw)

Tourist Panel with symbol

Figure 3-24

3.34 Fractions, to the nearest quarter of a mile, may be used for distances less than three miles. *Distances over 3 miles must be rounded to the nearest mile*. On motorway route confirmatory signs *all* distances must be to the nearest mile.

3.35 Where a destination contains both a distance and a route number, the latter must be placed on a separate line beneath the place name. The distance should be aligned vertically with the place name (except where shown otherwise in figure 4-12). Where a place name containing more than one word is shown on two lines, any distance should be centred vertically on the two lines.

3.36 Certain advance direction signs may show the distance to the junction ahead. Design details are covered in the sections dealing with map type signs for grade separated junctions (sections 5 and 10), dedicated lane advance direction signs (section 6) and gantry mounted signs (sections 9 and 10).

INDICATION OF ALTERNATIVE ROUTES

3.37 Item 32 of Schedule 16 to the Regulations permits the use on certain signs of a legend indicating an alternative route or a route avoiding a certain feature. The "alternative route" legend has an x-height that is 80% of the main x-height used on the sign. This requires special line and block spacing to take account of the reduced tile size. Figure 3-24 details the various vertical spaces that should be used. These are 0.5 sw greater than the standard spacing.

3.38 It should be noted that the first letter of the first word of the "alternative route" legend is in lower case. As shown in figure 3-24, the legend is ranged left below the destination to which it applies. Where the "alternative route" legend is on two or more lines each line is centred horizontally and the resulting block ranged left.

JUNCTION AND PLACE NAME PANELS

3.39 A junction or place name may be positioned at the top of either a map type or stack type advance direction sign in a separate sign panel as shown in figure 3-25. A sign may carry only one name; *this must have the same x-height as the main legend*. The name will always be in capital letters and may be on one or two lines.

3.40 The tiles are positioned on the sign panel so that the capital letters are equidistant from the top border and bottom panel divider. This is achieved by placing the tiles in the normal position (2.5 sw to the top border and 1.5 sw to the panel divider) and then lowering them by 0.3 sw (see para 2.17).

3.41 The panel divider has a width and an internal corner radius of 1.5 sw.

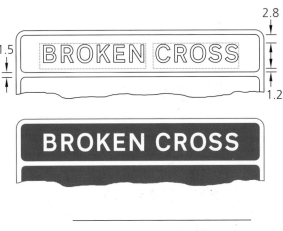

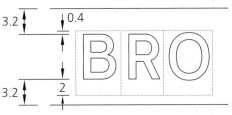

x-height same as main sign

Figure 3-25

USE OF BROWN TOURIST ATTRACTION PANELS

3.42 Although the Regulations permit the integration of brown tourist attraction panels into direction and advance direction signs, it might be cheaper and more efficient to place tourist information on a second sign. In diagram 2004 the inclusion of the tourist panel has resulted in wasted space under the "Dorfield" panel. On the other hand, in diagram 2113.1 removal of the tourist panel would not reduce the overall sign area. Where a separate tourist attraction sign is provided, such as diagram 2202, this should be sited at a convenient interval *after* the main sign. It is recommended that this segregation of information is maintained at the junction by providing a separate tourist attraction direction sign, such as diagram 2203.

4 STACK TYPE ADVANCE DIRECTION SIGNS

GENERAL DESIGN CONSIDERATIONS

4.1 Stack type signs are intended for use only at simple junctions and *should not indicate more than three directions* as the sign would then become difficult to read. Where four or more directions are to be signed a map type sign should be used. Stack type signs may supplement map type signs (i.e. where there are two advance direction signs on the approach to a junction and the first is a map type sign, the second may be a stack type sign).

4.2 There is some flexibility in the design of a stack type sign and figure 11-7 illustrates alternative layouts for the same junction. By careful arrangement of the directional panels the overall size of the sign can be minimised. In some cases, however, the smallest sign may not necessarily be the clearest and therefore should not be the automatic choice for a particular location.

DESIGN OF A SIMPLE STACK TYPE SIGN

4.3 The simplest type of stack type sign is one that indicates a single route, as shown in figure 4-1. The legend tiles will normally be 2.5 sw from the top border and 1.5 sw from the bottom border, in accordance with the basic sign design rules (see figure 2-4). Where the vertical dimension of the arrow determines the height of the sign, the legend is positioned so that the gap to the top border is greater than the gap to the bottom border by 1 sw. The arrow is always centred vertically on the sign, with a minimum gap of 2.5 sw to the top and bottom borders. Figure 4-2 shows the design of a sign with a legend panel. Both the arrow and the panel are centred vertically on the sign. Figure 4-3 shows how a stack type sign is designed to accommodate a single line legend with a patched route number. This follows design principles similar to those shown in figure 3-10.

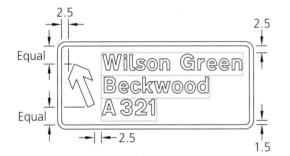

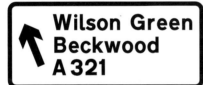

Height determined by legend

Height determined by arrow

Figure 4-1

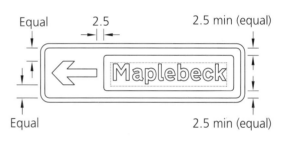

Figure 4-2

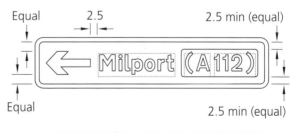

Figure 4-3

4.4 The design of the arrow is shown in figure 4-4. The length of 16 sw is reduced to 14 sw, by shortening the shaft, when a vertical arrow is used with a single line legend (tiles or panel). If the single line contains a symbol with a height greater than 14 sw, or the panel height exceeds 14 sw (because the panel includes a symbol), then a 16 sw arrow should be used.

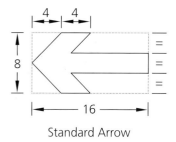

Standard Arrow

Figure 4-4

4.5 Figure 4-5 shows how the arrow may be inclined to suit the direction being indicated. Arrows may be vertical or horizontal or at any angle between in increments of 22.5°. Arrows shown in broken outline are used only in special circumstances. A special arrow may be used to indicate U-turns (e.g. at a roundabout on a dual carriageway); further details are given in section 14.

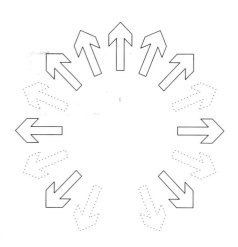

Figure 4-5

4.6 Where a sign has more than one directional panel, as shown in figure 4-6, the arrows should indicate the general direction of the individual route and ideally be at least 45° apart. Most junction layouts can be signed using the arrows shown with a continuous outline in figure 4-5. A vertical arrow should normally be placed on the left hand side of an advance direction sign. It may be placed on the right hand side of a rectangular direction sign. Further

This sign may reflect the true layout of the junction, but the two arrows are only 22.5° apart

This arrangement is preferred as the two arrows are 45° apart and give clearer indication of the turning movements at the junction ahead

Figure 4-6

guidance is given in Local Transport Note 1/94: The Design and Use of Directional Informatory Signs (to be superseded by Chapter 2).

4.7 Figure 4-7 shows the design of signs which include both tiled and panelled legends. The tiles or panel will be 2.5 sw from the top border, with a space to the bottom border of 1.5 sw for tiles and 2.5 sw for a panel. All destination blocks (tiles, panels and patches) are ranged left irrespective of the direction in which the arrow points.

4.8 Route number patches and symbols are treated the same as panels in determining the height of the sign. Symbols (other than warning triangles and regulatory roundels) are generally positioned at the opposite end of the legend to the arrow. *In the case of the "P" parking symbol, this should always be placed to the left of its associated legend unless this is the name of a tourist attraction.* The "P" symbol should then be placed between the legend and the tourist attraction symbol (if any). Where there is no tourist attraction symbol, the "P" symbol should

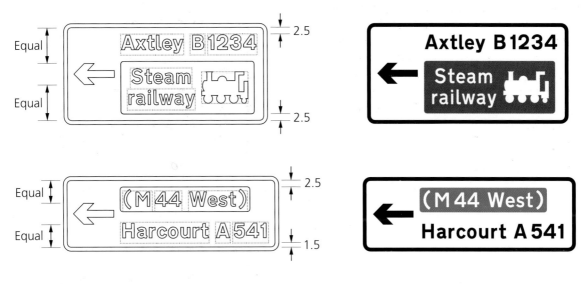

Figure 4-7

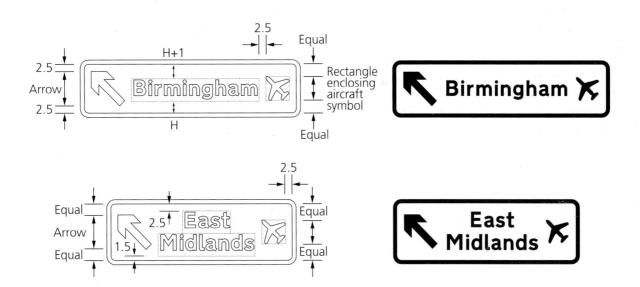

Figure 4-8

then be placed in accordance with the normal rules for symbols (i.e. at the opposite end of the tourist attraction name to the arrow). Where the aircraft symbol is used to denote an airport, this would generally be placed to the right of the airport name. Where the airport name is the same as the place name destination along the same route, the aircraft symbol may be used on its own on a separate line ranged left. For some sign face designs it may be appropriate to centre a symbol above or below its associated legend (e.g. lorry or ferry symbol).

4.9 Many symbols have a directional element to their design and these are listed at Appendix B. If the arrow is pointing ahead or left (at any angle) the symbol should face left, otherwise the symbol should face right. The aircraft symbol may be rotated to point in the same direction as the arrow, except that the symbol should never point below the horizontal. Where the arrow inclines downwards the aircraft symbol should be horizontal, facing left or right as appropriate. Figure 4-8 shows how an inclined aircraft symbol is positioned alongside a tiled legend.

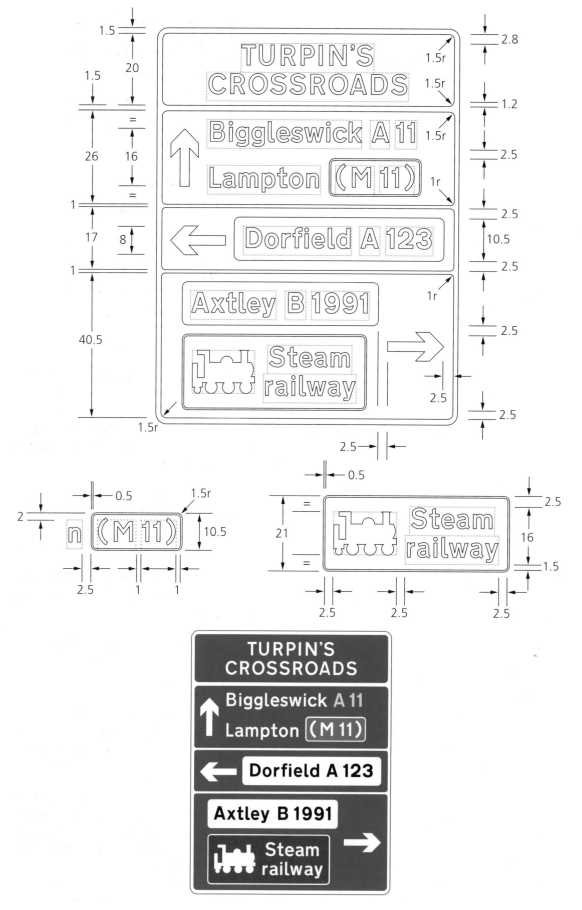

Figure 4-9 (diagram 2005)

COMPLEX STACK TYPE SIGN DESIGN

4.10 The design of diagram 2005 is shown in figure 4-9 and is in the form of a working drawing.

4.11 The sign comprises two sections as described in para 2.19. These are the junction name at the top and the directional information given below. The general rule, as set out in para 2.19, is that a divider separating different elements of the sign will have the same width as the sign border (usually 1.5 sw). However, on a stack type directional sign all routes indicated are considered to be one sign element. Therefore the dividers between the different routes have a reduced width of 1 sw. The junction name is a different element and therefore has a divider 1.5 sw wide. The corner radii are equal to the width of the divider to which they relate (as shown in figure 4-9). Design of the junction name panel is described in paras 3.39 to 3.41.

4.12 The general order in which directions are indicated is as follows:-

(a) Ahead destination with vertical arrow on left hand side of destination block.

(b) Destinations to the left with the arrow to the left of the destination block. Where more than one left turn is shown the order from top to bottom is *anti-clockwise.*

(c) Destinations to the right with the arrow to the right of the destination block. Where more than one right turn is shown the order from top to bottom is *clockwise.*

4.13 In some cases the order in which the various directions are shown, as set out in para 4.12, may be varied to produce a more balanced sign layout. For example a two-panel sign might have one arrow pointing downwards at 45° to the left and the other arrow pointing upwards at 45° to the right. Showing the right turn above the left turn would, in this case, improve the appearance of the sign, as shown in figure 4-10.

4.14 For the design of diagram 2005 illustrated in figure 4-9 the points to consider are:-

(a) "Biggleswick" and "Lampton" are two different blocks, being associated with different route numbers. As the "M11" patch is directly below the

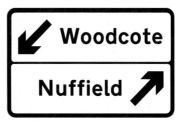

Normal stacking order

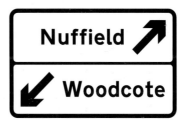

Improved stacking order

Figure 4-10

"A11" tiles, the appropriate block spacing of 2.5 sw is chosen (see para 3.25) and this is measured to the outside border of the patch. The "M11" patch rather than the tiled legend "Lampton" determines the space to the lower panel divider. The arrow is centred vertically on the sign panel.

(b) The width of the sign is determined by the left turn destination. The ahead destinations are ranged left and positioned on the left hand side of the sign panel so that the vertical arrow is 2.5 sw from the left hand border. The right turn destinations are ranged left and positioned on the right hand side of the sign panel so that the horizontal arrow is 2.5 sw from the right hand border.

4.15 Figure 4-11 illustrates the design of the sign shown in diagram 2103. The additional design features to consider are:-

(a) Where distances are shown in a list of destinations they are centred above each other. The minimum horizontal space between any place name (or route number) and a distance on either the same line, the line immediately above or the line immediately below is 7 sw. *As the "(A1(M))" patch is in this case a destination rather than a route number (i.e. it has no associated place name), a distance may be shown on the same line.* Where a destination includes a place name, a route number and a distance, the route number must be shown on a separate line, e.g."Millington Green (A 4011)".

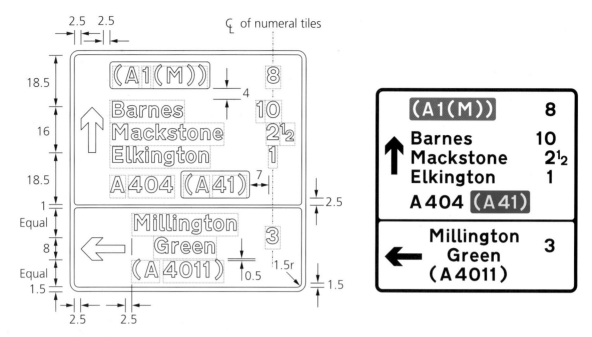

Figure 4-11 (diagram 2103)

Mileage tiles on adjacent lines may overlap horizontally (e.g. "10" and "2¹/2"). Where more than one distance is 10 miles or greater, the "tens" column is centred in the same way as the "units" column. This may result in a gap between some tiles making up a distance of two figures. The "3" in the lower sign panel is shown as being on the same centre line as the numerals in the upper sign panel. This is optional, and is recommended only where the shortest horizontal space between the destination and distance in any one sign panel does not extend too far beyond 7 sw. The effect on the overall appearance of the sign should be the deciding factor. See paras 3.32 to 3.36 for use of distances.

(b) *Fractions are not used for distances greater than 3 miles* (see para 3.34).

(c) Destinations are generally ranged left. However where a destination of two or more words, such as "Millington Green", is placed on two lines, these are centred horizontally.

(d) Where a motorway number is in the form "A1(M)", the gap between the last numeral and the bracket before the "M" is 1 sw. When the motorway number is bracketed the tiles of the two adjacent closing brackets are butted together.

(e) The "g" tile of "Elkington" is horizontally within 2.5 sw of the "(A 41)" patch and hence the vertical gap (line spacing) is 1 sw (see para 3.24).

TRIANGULAR WARNING SIGNS ON STACK TYPE SIGNS

4.16 Figure 4-12 shows how triangular warning signs are added to stack type signs. The triangle is always placed on the same side of the legend as the arrow. Where the sign has a green, blue or brown background *a white edge is added to the outside of the triangle*. The appropriate heights for the triangles (excluding any white edges) are given in Appendix D. A distance plate to diagram 572 may be added below the triangle, as shown in figure 4-12. The plate is designed as a normal sign and then reduced to 80% of its size. Thus if the x-height of the main sign is 100 mm, the x-height of the plate will be 80 mm. Where the plate is placed on a green, blue or brown background the border is omitted, the corner radii remaining at 1.5 sw based on the plate x-height (i.e. 1.2 sw based on the x-height of the main sign).

4.17 Where a destination is shown on a panel, the warning triangle is also included in that panel.

4.18 Where a destination is indicated to the right, any distance is generally placed to the right of the warning sign. However, where more than one destination is shown, the clarity of the sign is improved by placing the distances to the left of the warning triangle, as shown in the top diagram of figure 4-12.

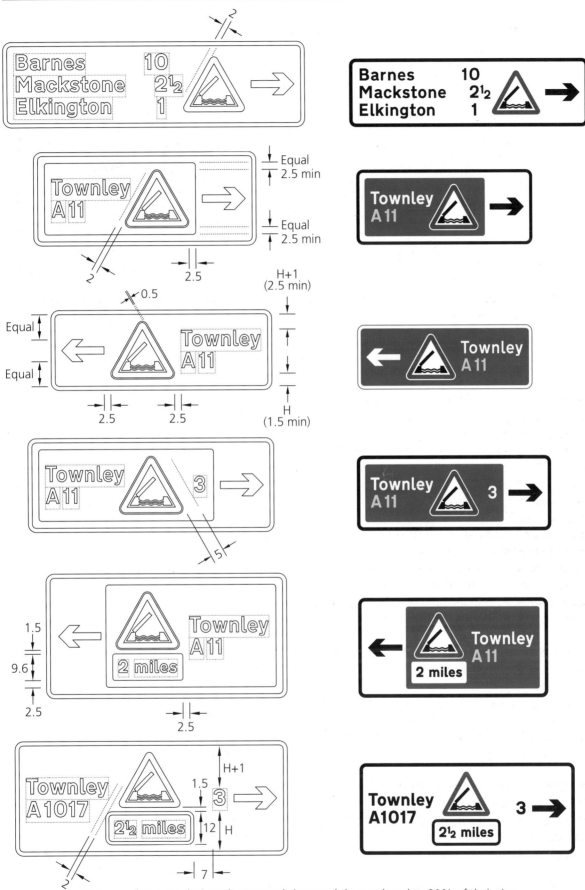

Distance plates are designed as normal signs and then reduced to 80% of their size.

All dimensions are in stroke widths based on the main x-height.

Figure 4-12

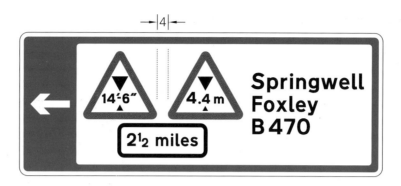

Figure 4-13

4.19 On some stack type signs it may be desirable to show two warning triangles, such as imperial and metric height limits or two different hazards along the same route. An example is shown in figure 4-13. Any metric sign must always be placed to the right of the imperial sign. *A metric sign cannot be used by itself*. Where two triangular signs indicate different hazards associated with the same route, and they have different heights, the larger height should be used for both triangles. Where a distance plate is used with imperial and metric signs, this should be centred horizontally beneath the two triangles. Where two triangular signs indicate different hazards, any distance plate should be associated with the appropriate sign. Where this would result in the two triangles being further apart than 6 stroke widths it is strongly recommended that the triangles be omitted from the sign and separate signing used to indicate the hazards.

4.20 The dimensions relating to the various gaps apply equally to plates with and without borders and to triangles with and without white edges. The gap is measured to the outside of any border or edge provided.

REGULATORY SIGNS ON STACK TYPE SIGNS

4.21 Figures 4-14 and 4-15 show how regulatory sign roundels are added to stack type signs. The roundel is always placed on the same side of the legend as the arrow. Where the sign has a green, blue or brown background *a white edge is added to the outside of the roundel*. The appropriate diameters for the roundels (excluding any white edges) are given in Appendix D. *A plate indicating the distance from the junction to the restriction should always be used unless the restriction indicated commences at the junction.* The design of the plate is the same as described for distance plates in para 4.16. Where the plate is placed on a green, blue or brown background the border is omitted.

4.22 Where a destination is shown on a panel, the roundel and any plate is also included in that panel.

4.23 Figure 4-15 includes the alternative route message, the design of which is detailed in paras 3.37 and 3.38.

4.24 Two roundels may be shown in a similar manner as described for warning triangles in para 4.19. An example is shown in figure 4-16.

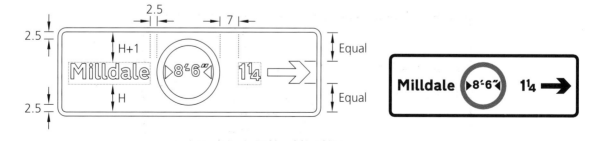

Figure 4-14

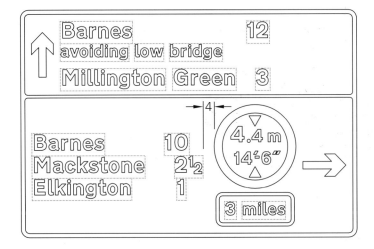

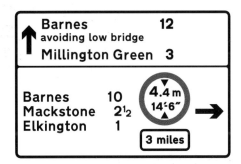

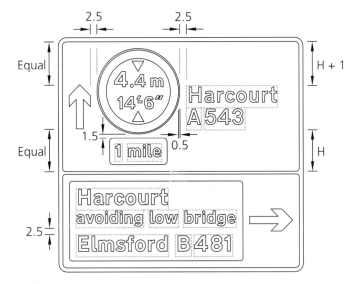

All dimensions are in stroke widths based on the main x-height

NOTE

"1 mile" and "avoiding low bridge" have an x-height equal to 80% of the main x-height. The "1 mile" plate is designed in accordance with the normal design rules appropriate to its reduced x-height.

Figure 4-15

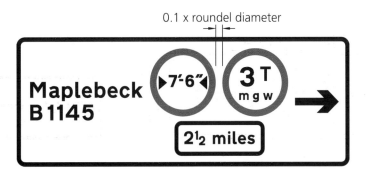

Figure 4-16

4.25 Where a destination is indicated to the right, any distance is generally placed to the right of the regulatory sign. However, where more than one destination is shown, the clarity of the sign is improved by placing the distances between the place names and the regulatory roundel, as shown in figure 4-15.

4.26 The dimensions relating to the various gaps apply equally to plates with and without borders and to roundels with and without white edges. The gap is measured to the outside of any border or edge provided.

REGULATORY AND WARNING SIGNS ASSOCIATED WITH THE SAME DESTINATION

4.27 There may be occasions where it is required to show both a regulatory and a triangular warning sign on the same directional panel. An example is shown in figure 4-17. The diameter of the roundel and the height of the triangle should both be the same, based on the size of the larger sign as listed in Appendix D.

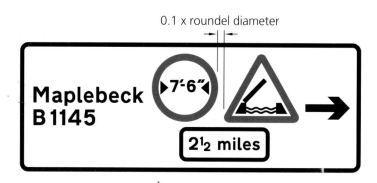

Figure 4-17

5 MAP TYPE ADVANCE DIRECTION SIGNS

GENERAL DESIGN CONSIDERATIONS

5.1 Although the geometric layout of the junction will, in general, determine the design of a map type sign, there is flexibility in adjusting the shape of the route symbol and in the positioning of destination blocks and panels. Some designs may be more pleasing in appearance or more economical than others and in many cases can improve the clarity of the sign. See figures 11-8 to 11-12 for illustrations of alternative layouts for a selection of signs.

WIDTH OF ROUTE ARMS

5.2 The width of each route arm on map type signs is generally related to the status of the route indicated. 6 sw is used for primary routes and motorways, 4 sw for numbered non-primary routes and 2.5 sw for unnumbered local routes. Where a bracketed route number is indicated along an unnumbered local route, the route arm width is 4 sw. An example of a sign showing the various route arm widths is shown in figure 5-1. A special width of 5 sw is used for all routes indicated on a grade separated junction advance direction sign (see figure 5-11). A width of 5 sw is also used for the approach arm on the special map type roundabout sign located on the exit slip road at a grade separated junction (see figure 5-24).

Primary route.
Route arm 6 sw wide

Non-primary route.
Route arm 4 sw wide

Leeds
A 63

Tadcaster
B 1223

Doncaster
(A 19)

Barlby

Local unnumbered route with bracketed route number.
Route arm 4 sw wide

Local unnumbered route.
Route arm 2.5 sw wide

Figure 5-1

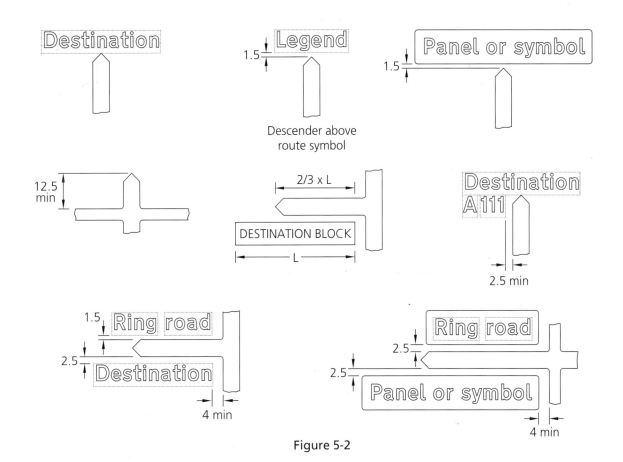

Destination

Legend
1.5
Descender above route symbol

Panel or symbol
1.5

12.5 min

2/3 x L
DESTINATION BLOCK
L

Destination
A 111
2.5 min

1.5 Ring road
2.5 Destination
4 min

Ring road
2.5
2.5 Panel or symbol
4 min

Figure 5-2

41

VERTICAL AND HORIZONTAL ROUTE ARMS

5.3 The appropriate spacings between different types of legend (tiles or panels) and the vertical and horizontal route arms are shown in figure 5-2. The horizontal gaps measured to the vertical route arm are minimum values. The exact dimension will depend on the overall design of a particular sign.

5.4 Where a tiled legend with a descender is placed over a vertical route arm, the vertical gap can be reduced to zero when the descender tile is at least 2.5 sw horizontally from the nearest vertical face of the arm. This also applies where there is a patch or symbol on the same line as the tiled legend.

5.5 The minimum length of a vertical route arm is 12.5 sw. This is to ensure the correct spacing between the forward destination and the horizontal route arm (see para 5.22).

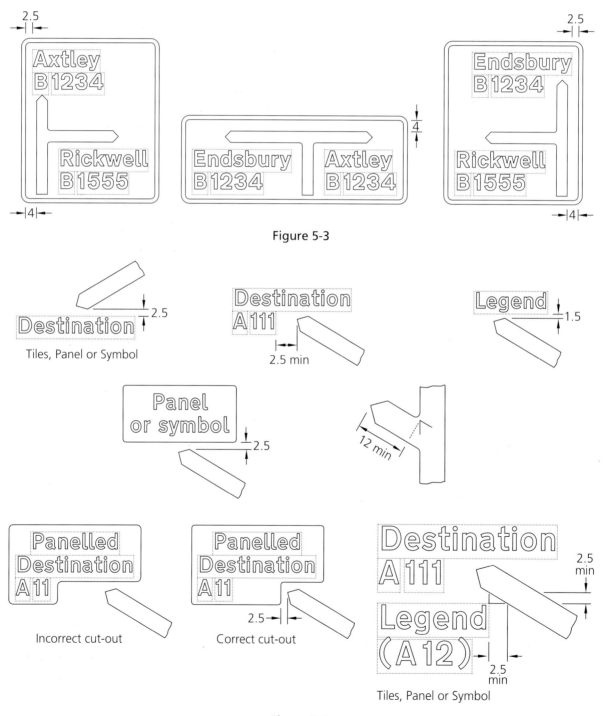

Figure 5-3

Figure 5-4

5.6 The horizontal route arm extends to a point two thirds along the length of the destination block (tiles or panel) as shown in figure 5-2. The measurement should be based on the longest block associated with a particular direction, but see paras 5.39, 5.63, 5.71 and 11.17 for exceptions.

5.7 Where a map type sign indicates destinations both to the left and to the right, the vertical route symbol will generally be in the central part of the sign. The associated destination block will be centred horizontally above the route symbol. Where destinations are indicated to the left or to the right, but not in both directions, the vertical route symbol will be placed adjacent to the appropriate side border. Figure 5-3 shows the appropriate dimensions for positioning the route symbol and the associated forward destination block. When the route symbol is on the right hand side of the sign, it may be possible to tuck the symbol into a multi-line legend as shown.

INCLINED ROUTE ARMS

5.8 In most cases the vertical or horizontal space between an inclined route arm and any type of legend is 2.5 sw. This is reduced to 1.5 sw when a tiled legend is placed directly above the route arm. Examples are given in figure 5-4.

5.9 With some arrangements it may be possible to tuck the route arm into the legend as shown in figure 5-4.

5.10 For an upward pointing route arm less than 15° from the vertical, the dimensions associated with a vertical arm may be adopted.

5.11 Where a panel has a cut-out, this must only be sufficient to allow the route arm to tuck in. The outer edge of the panel will not necessarily follow the outline of the tiled legend (see figure 5-4).

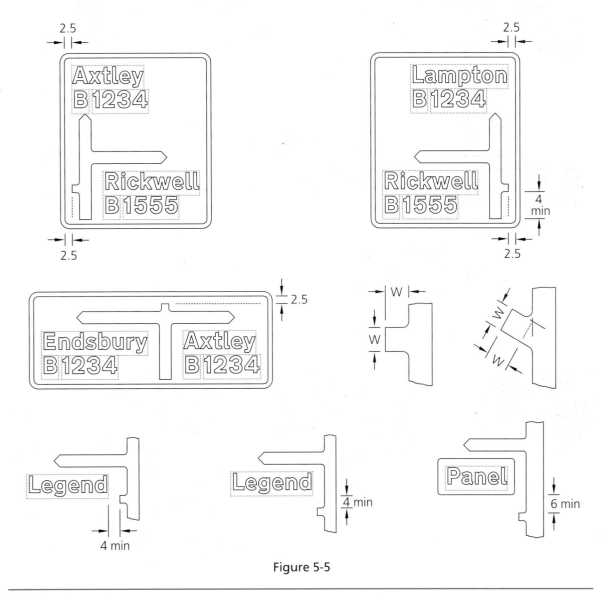

Figure 5-5

5.12 The minimum length of route arm is 12 sw measured along the shortest side, as shown in figure 5-4. This does not apply to the side arm of the grade separated junction symbol, which has a minimum length of 24 sw measured along the centre line (see figure 5-11).

DESIGN OF ROUTE SYMBOL STUBS

5.13 Where no destinations are indicated in a particular direction, a stub replaces the full length route arm. The length of the stub is generally equal to its width, which in turn will depend on the status of the route (see figure 5-1). Figure 5-5 details the dimensions of the stub and includes the relevant spacing to legend and border. See para 5.82 for the design of stubs which include the "no through road" symbol.

UNRELATED BLOCKS

5.14 On a map type sign, destinations associated with different routes leading from a junction ahead are known as unrelated blocks. It is important that these blocks are properly positioned on the sign so that there is no confusion in associating each block with the correct route symbol.

5.15 Where one block is directly above another, the vertical space between them should be a minimum of 12 sw. If the upper block is a panel or contains a patch or symbol on the bottom line, then the vertical space is increased to 14 sw. This is to take account of the 2 sw space at the bottom of a tiled legend (i.e. when the upper block is tiled, the actual space between the lower block and the bottom of the letters of the upper block, ignoring descenders, is 14 sw).

5.16 Where two blocks are alongside each other, the horizontal space between them should be a minimum of 12 sw for all types of legend.

5.17 Where a block is above and to one side of another block, it should be positioned as shown in figure 5-6.

DESIGN OF A MAP TYPE ADVANCE DIRECTION SIGN

5.18 The design of a complete map type sign is shown in figure 5-7, in the form of a working drawing for diagram 2004.

5.19 The base of the approach arm of the route symbol for *all* map type signs is 1.5 sw from the bottom border. Where the approach arm is curved (e.g. junction on a bend), there should be a vertical section, with a minimum length equal to the width of the arm, before the start of the curve.

5.20 Where two route arms join, there is a fillet of 1 sw radius.

5.21 The horizontal route arm extends to a point two thirds along the length of the legend block, as shown in figure 5-2. The measurement is always based on the longest block associated with a particular direction. Where a particular route has no associated destinations, the route arm is either replaced by a square ended stub that has a length equal to its width (see figure 5-5) or, if appropriate, shown as a "no through road" (see para 5.82).

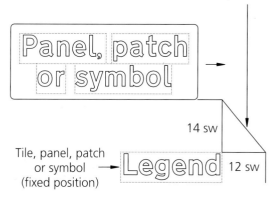

Figure 5-6

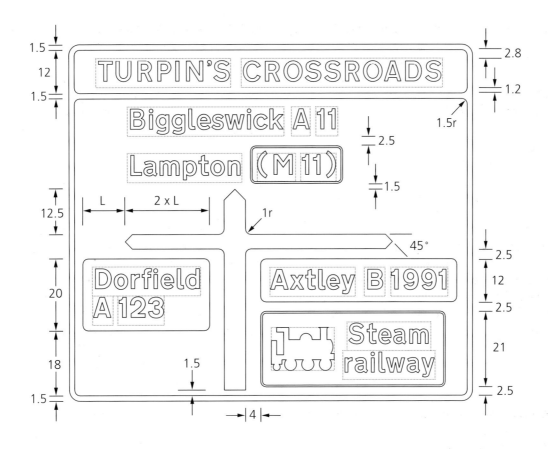

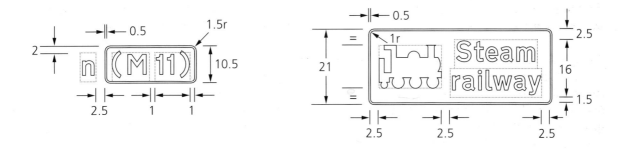

Figure 5-7 (diagram 2004)

5.22 The minimum vertical distance between the horizontal route arm and the forward legend above is 12 sw for tiles and 14 sw for panels, patches and symbols. The gap is larger for panels than for tiles, to take account of the 2 sw space between the letters and the bottom of the tiles. For simplicity, the minimum length of the forward arm should be taken as 12.5 sw. This gives 14 sw between the horizontal route arm and any panel or patch above (12.5 sw route arm length plus 1.5 sw gap from the route arm to the panel). Where tiles are placed directly on the route arm, the vertical distance will be 12.5 sw rather than 12 sw. However, some designs allow a line of legend to be placed alongside the vertical route arm. Diagram 2109 is a good example (see figure 5-8). In this case the minimum distance of 12 sw between legend tiles and horizontal route arm should be used.

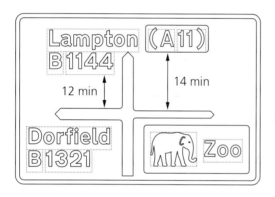

Figure 5-8 (diagram 2109)

5.23 For the design of diagram 2004 illustrated in figure 5-7 the points to consider are :-

(a) "Biggleswick" and "Lampton" are two different blocks, being associated with different route numbers. As the "M11" patch is directly below the "A11" tiles, the appropriate block spacing of 2.5 sw is chosen, measured to the outside border of the patch.

(b) The width of the sign and the position of the vertical route arm are both determined by the left and right turn destinations.

(c) The longest ahead destination is centred horizontally over the vertical route arm and the other destination ranged left. (Note: all destinations associated with the same route are generally ranged left.) The centring rule applies only where there are side destinations both to the left and to the right (see para 5.7).

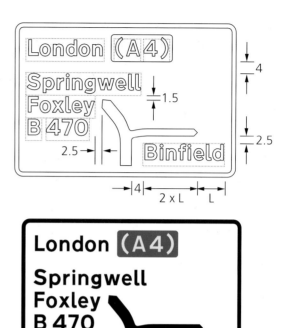

Figure 5-9 (diagram 2102)

(d) As the "M11" patch is within 2.5 sw horizontally of the right hand edge of the vertical route arm, it is placed 1.5 sw above the point of the arm. Had the patch been more than 2.5 sw from the arm, it would have been possible to have extended the arm to touch the tiles above. However, it would not have been possible to lower the legend block to touch the symbol (thus reducing the overall height of the sign) since the resulting gap between the "M11" patch and the horizontal route arm would then be less than 14 sw.

(e) The pointed end of the right hand route arm will be two thirds along the "Axtley" panel, which is the longest destination associated with the right turn.

(f) The side turn route arms are both 4 sw wide because they indicate numbered non-primary routes.

5.24 Figure 5-9 illustrates the design of the sign shown in diagram 2102. The additional design features to consider are :-

(a) The symbol for the through route is curved to reflect the alignment of the junction. This enables the inclined route arm to tuck into the legend block. The "Springwell, Foxley" block, with the route number "B 470" repositioned alongside to the right, could have been placed over the route symbol, but this would have increased the overall height of the sign.

The design as shown in figure 5-9 is not only more economical but also emphasises the change in direction at the junction. With this type of layout it is important that the ahead destination block is not too close to the bottom of the sign. It is better for this block to be positioned higher than any other blocks on the sign.

(b) "London (A 4)" is a separate block and the appropriate vertical space to the "Springwell" block is 4 sw (patch with tiles below). However, had the place name in the "London" block been longer, so that the left hand edge of the patch was horizontally 6 sw or more to the right of "Springwell", it would have been possible to have reduced the block spacing to 2 sw (tiles with tiles below) in accordance with para 3.27.

5.25 The layout of the route symbols should reflect the actual road layout at the junction. However, in many situations it will be appropriate to simplify the design. For example, where the side arm is, in reality, 94° to the vertical it is better to show this as 90° on the sign. Complicated junctions should be indicated on the sign in a manner which can be easily understood by the road user.

MAJOR-MINOR PRIORITY JUNCTIONS ON DUAL CARRIAGEWAY ROADS

5.26 Figure 5-10 shows various designs for route symbols indicating crossroads and staggered junctions on dual carriageways. One half of the staggered junction symbol can be used to indicate a single turning either to the left or to the right.

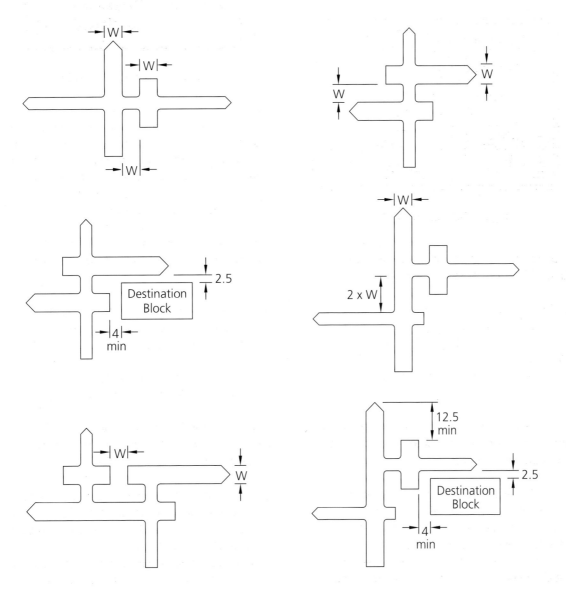

Figure 5-10

47

DESIGN OF MAP TYPE SIGNS FOR GRADE SEPARATED JUNCTIONS ON ALL-PURPOSE ROADS

5.27 Figure 5-11 illustrates signs shown in diagrams 2101.1 and 2101.2. The design of these follows the general principles for map type signs, but there are special features which are detailed below.

5.28 The route symbol is always 5 sw wide (both arms) irrespective of the status of the routes indicated.

5.29 The intersection point of the vertical arm and the lower edge of the side arm is 7 sw measured from the bottom of the vertical arm. The side arm is inclined at 60° to the vertical. Although permitted by

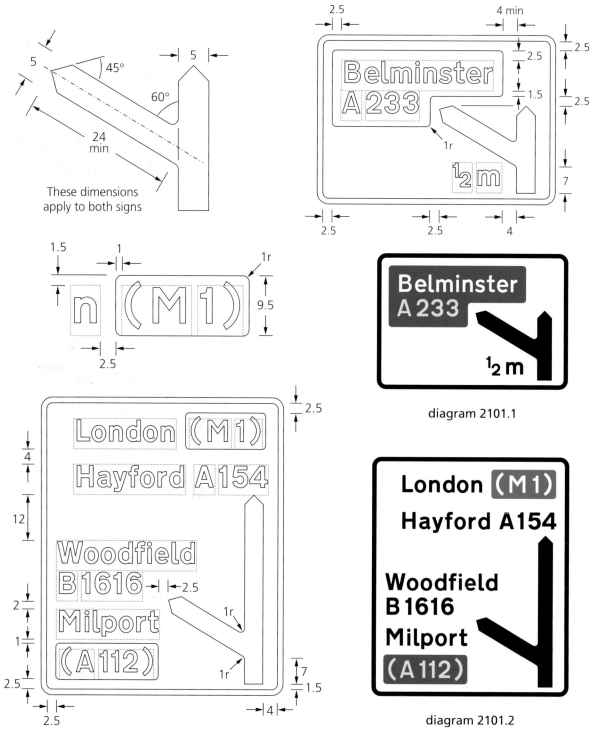

diagram 2101.1

diagram 2101.2

Figure 5-11

the Regulations, there should be no changes to the overall shape of the symbol unless there are exceptional circumstances.

5.30 The minimum length of the side arm is 24 sw measured along its centre line from the left hand edge of the vertical arm.

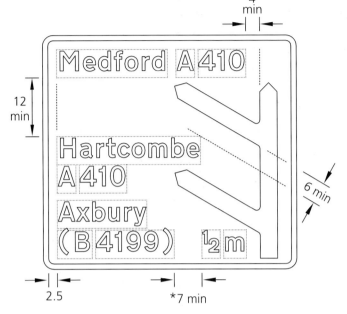

diagram 2013 (variant)

*This dimension applies when destination block is alongside as shown or is less than 2 sw above the top of the distance tiles.

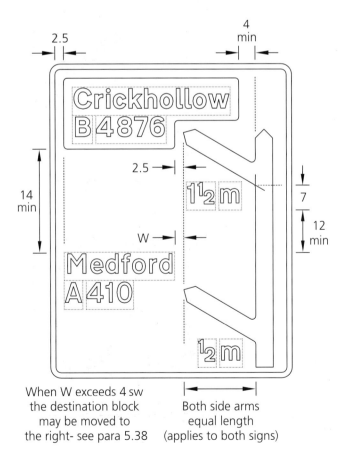

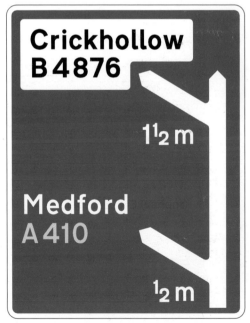

diagram 2013 (variant)

When W exceeds 4 sw the destination block may be moved to the right- see para 5.38

Both side arms equal length (applies to both signs)

Figure 5-12

5.31 The vertical arm is always 4 sw from the right hand border, unless it incorporates a triangular warning sign or regulatory sign roundel (see para 5.65).

5.32 For 1 mile and 1/2 mile advance direction signs without forward destinations (see diagram 2101.1 in figure 5-11) the highest parts of the forward and side arm route symbols are always at the same level.

5.33 The side destination blocks may extend to the bottom of the sign, as shown in diagram 2101.2. Note that the legend "Woodfield" is more than 1.5 sw above the route arm. It is not appropriate to move the arm vertically to close this gap.

5.34 Where a sign includes forward destinations, as shown in diagram 2101.2, it should be designed so that the forward destination blocks are not further to the left than the side destination blocks. To achieve this it may be necessary to extend the length of the side arm.

5.35 The minimum vertical distance between the side destination block(s) and the forward destination block(s) is 12 sw. This is increased to 14 sw when the bottom line of the forward destination block is a panel or contains a patch or symbol directly above the top line of the side destination block (see para 5.15).

5.36 A junction name, *but not a place name*, may be added to the top of the *first* advance direction sign (see paras 3.39 to 3.41).

5.37 The distance to the junction, as shown in diagram 2101.1, may be 1m, 2/3m, 1/2m or 1/3m. Any other distance will require special authorisation. Where a side destination is placed alongside the distance to the junction, there should be a minimum horizontal gap of 7 sw (see figure 5-12). Distances to destinations are not permitted on grade separated junction signs as they could be confused with distances to the junction. Mileages are normally shown on route confirmatory signs provided after

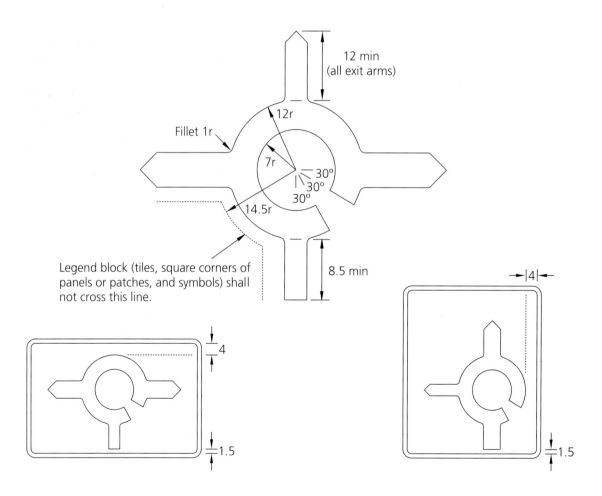

Figure 5-13

50

the junction. They may also be shown on advance direction signs on exit slip roads.

5.38 Some junction layouts have two consecutive exit slip roads, and a sign to diagram 2013 (or non-primary route equivalent) would be appropriate. It is also possible that two junctions are so close together that it is not practicable to sign each one separately. In this case a variant of diagram 2013 is used, showing the distance to each junction. The additional design details for grade separated junction signs with two side arms are shown in figure 5-12. Both side arms should be the same length and, where possible, all destination blocks should be ranged left. Where a block ranged left would be spaced more than 4 sw horizontally from its associated route arm, the block may be moved to the right to ensure that it is still associated with the arm. It should be noted that these signs must not include forward destinations. The final advance direction sign for the first exit slip road should be to diagram 2014 or 2101.2, with forward destinations that include those places reached by leaving at the second exit.

MAP TYPE SIGNS FOR NORMAL ROUNDABOUTS

5.39 Figure 5-13 shows the basic design of the route symbol and the appropriate gaps to the sign borders. The roundabout itself always has a width of 5 sw, whatever the status of the routes at the junction. The approach and exit arms follow the normal design rules, except that the minimum length of any exit arm is 12 sw. The minimum length of the approach arm is 8.5 sw (there is no maximum length).

5.40 Where the right turn arm is below the horizontal, the cut-out in the roundabout symbol has to be adjusted. An example is shown in figure 5-14. The recommended minimum angle for the cut-out is 25°. It may be necessary to move the approach arm to the left, as shown in figure 5-15. The purpose of the cut-out is to emphasise that all traffic must travel in a clockwise direction.

5.41 Where a roundabout is offset from the main direction of travel, it may be appropriate to show a curved approach arm on the advance direction sign. An example is shown in figure 5-16.

5.42 Where two normal roundabouts are close together, or form a single junction, a special symbol is used. This is shown in figure 5-17, together with typical variations in layout. It should be noted that the two roundabout symbols never touch each other and that the connector between them is always 5 sw wide, irrespective of the status of the various routes at the junction. The connector may be lengthened should this reflect the actual road geometry more accurately.

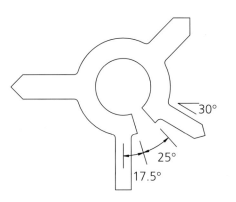

Figure 5-14

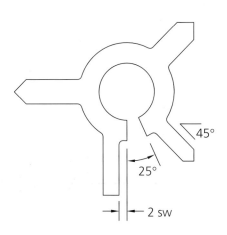

Figure 5-15

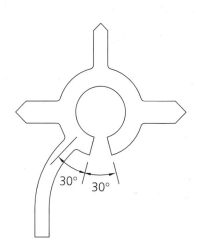

Figure 5-16

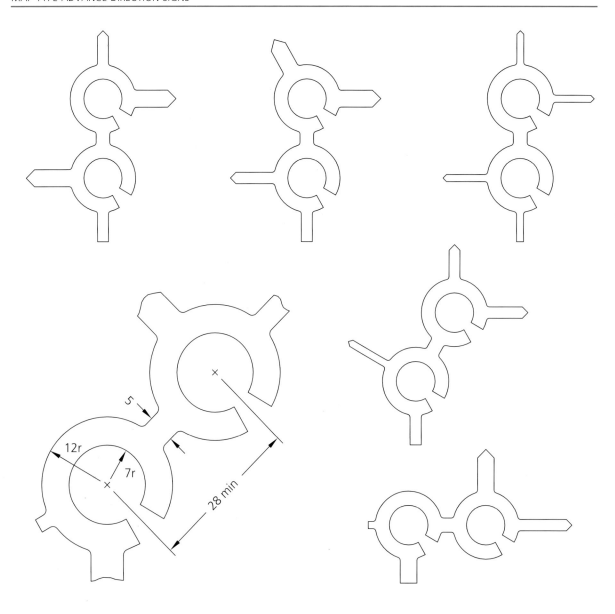

Figure 5-17

MAP TYPE SIGNS FOR ROUNDABOUTS WITH PRIORITY LEFT TURN LANES

5.43 Figure 5-18 shows the basic design of the route symbol which should be used where a priority lane is segregated from the roundabout either by ghost markings or by a solid island. The symbol design remains the same for both diverge/merge and lane drop/lane gain situations. The width of the priority lane is always 2.5 sw, regardless of the status of the route. The remainder of the roundabout symbol is designed in accordance with the details given in paras 5.39 and 5.40.

5.44 The basic design is applicable to left turn route arms that are angled between 30° above the horizontal and 30° below the horizontal, as shown in figure 5-19. Where the arm is inclined at a greater angle, the design has to be adjusted. Figure 5-20 shows that with the arm pointing downwards at 45°, the radius of the priority lane has to be reduced to 7.5 sw. The gap between the lane and the roundabout is increased from the normal 2 sw. Figure 5-21 shows that with the arm pointing upwards at 60°, the priority lane can be accommodated by offsetting the roundabout symbol to the right. However, in this case it may be necessary to adjust the design of the symbol should it not reflect the actual road geometry.

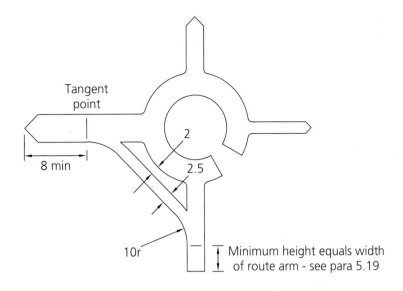

Figure 5-18

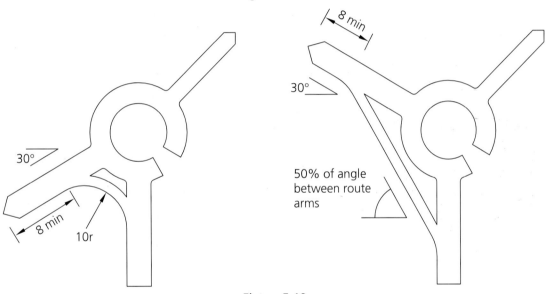

Figure 5-19

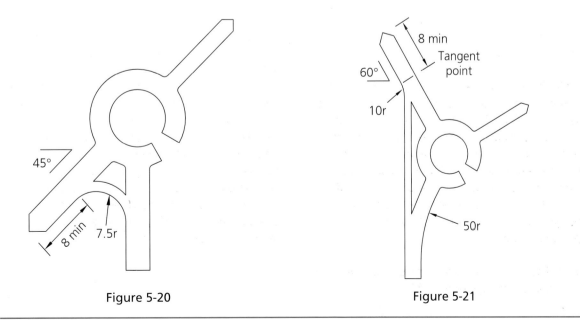

Figure 5-20   **Figure 5-21**

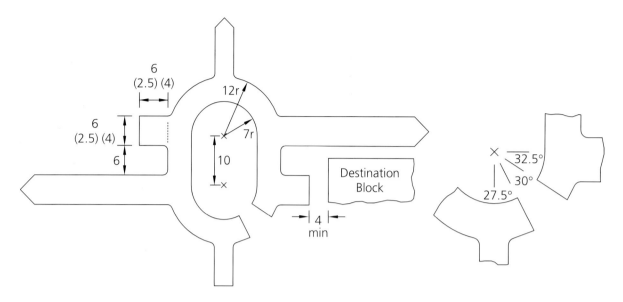

Figure 5-22

MAP TYPE SIGNS FOR ROUNDABOUTS AT GRADE SEPARATED JUNCTIONS

5.45 Figure 5-22 shows the basic design of the route symbol when approaching from the side road. All route arms and stubs have a thickness appropriate to the route indicated. The design can be adjusted to suit the circumstances, such as indicating an additional exit from the roundabout. The oval roundabout and side arms can be rotated, as shown in figure 5-23, if this best illustrates the true layout of the junction.

5.46 Figure 5-24 shows the basic design of the route symbol when approaching from the exit slip road of either a motorway or an all-purpose road. The approach arm and stubs opposite are always 5 sw wide regardless of the status of the route (this is consistent with the map type advance direction signs on the main carriageway which also have a width of 5 sw - see para 5.28). The side arms have a width appropriate to the status of the route indicated. It is possible to adjust the design to suit the circumstances; an example is shown in figure 5-25. Some grade separated junctions on three levels have slip roads on two major routes, with an interconnecting roundabout. The design of the roundabout symbol is shown in figure 5-26.

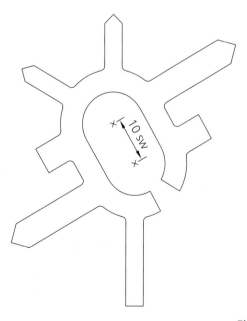

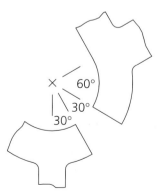

Figure 5-23

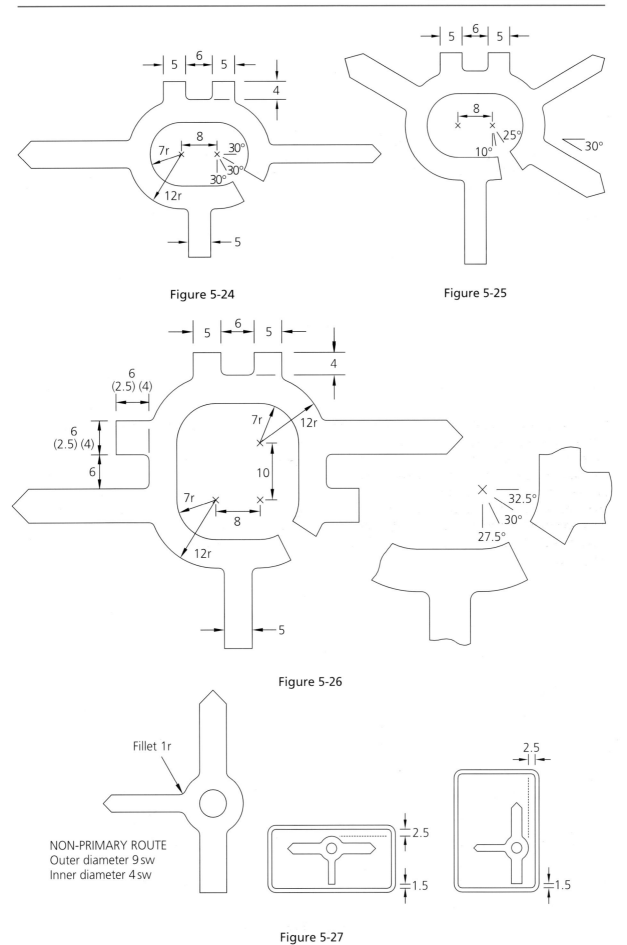

Figure 5-24

Figure 5-25

Figure 5-26

NON-PRIMARY ROUTE
Outer diameter 9 sw
Inner diameter 4 sw

Fillet 1r

Figure 5-27

MAP TYPE SIGNS FOR MINI-ROUNDABOUTS

5.47 Figure 5-27 shows the design of the route symbol for a single mini-roundabout on a non-primary route. Note that, unlike the normal roundabout, there is no cut-out in the symbol. The design is used when all arms, including the approach arm, have a width of either 4 sw or 2.5 sw. Figure 5-28 shows the equivalent design for a primary route where at least one arm, which could be the approach arm, has a width of 6 sw (the larger diameters take account of the wider route arms). *The Regulations do not permit the mini-roundabout sign shown in diagram 611.1 to be used as a symbol on map type signs.*

5.48 Figure 5-29 shows the design of the route symbol for a double mini-roundabout on a non-primary route. The connector between the two roundabouts is *always 4 sw wide*, even if all route arms have a width of 2.5 sw. The orientation of the symbol can be varied to suit the circumstances.

5.49 Figure 5-30 shows the design of the route symbol for a double mini-roundabout on a primary route. The connector between the two roundabouts is *always 6 sw wide*, even if all route arms leading off the second roundabout have a width less than 6 sw. The orientation of the symbol can be varied to suit the circumstances.

5.50 Any legend should not come closer than 2.5 sw to the roundabout symbol, as for normal roundabouts (see figure 5-13).

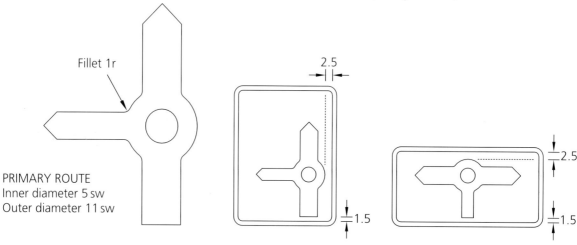

Fillet 1r

PRIMARY ROUTE
Inner diameter 5 sw
Outer diameter 11 sw

2.5

2.5

1.5

1.5

Figure 5-28

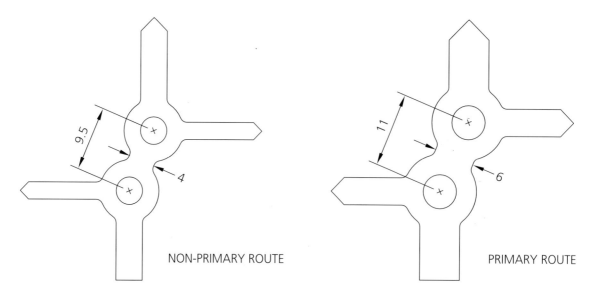

NON-PRIMARY ROUTE

9.5

4

PRIMARY ROUTE

11

6

Figure 5-29

Figure 5-30

MAP TYPE SIGNS FOR IRREGULARLY SHAPED ROUNDABOUTS AND GYRATORY SYSTEMS

5.51 Figure 5-31 gives examples of map type signs for junctions where the normal roundabout symbol does not reflect the actual road layout. For gyratory systems it is usually more appropriate to use a symbol width relating to the status of the route through the junction, rather than the special width of 5 sw. For irregularly shaped roundabouts the symbol width of 5 sw will be appropriate in most cases.

5.52 A special type of roundabout is the dumb-bell. This is where two adjacent roundabouts are joined to form a gyratory system. They are likely to be used where (a) a bridge between the two roundabouts precludes the construction of a single large roundabout (some grade separated junctions are purposely designed like this to economise on the provision of structures), or (b) traffic congestion between two roundabouts can be eased by the formation of a gyratory system.

5.53 The design of the map type symbols for dumb-bell roundabouts is shown in figure 5-32. Where the route is through the two partial roundabouts, the complete road layout is shown. However, in the case of an exit slip road at a grade separated junction where there are limited turning movements (i.e. a single left turn and a single right turn) a simplified symbol, as shown in figure 5-32, may be used. It should be noted that for this simplified symbol the width of the right turn route arm is 5 sw, irrespective of the status of the route. Simplified symbols, showing only the first part of the junction, may also be used where an advance direction sign is provided between the two partial roundabouts.

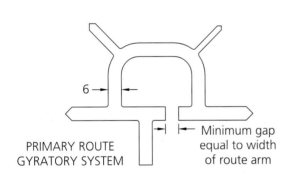
PRIMARY ROUTE GYRATORY SYSTEM

Minimum gap equal to width of route arm

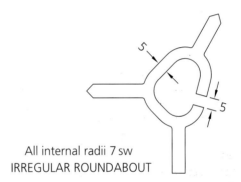
All internal radii 7 sw
IRREGULAR ROUNDABOUT

Figure 5-31

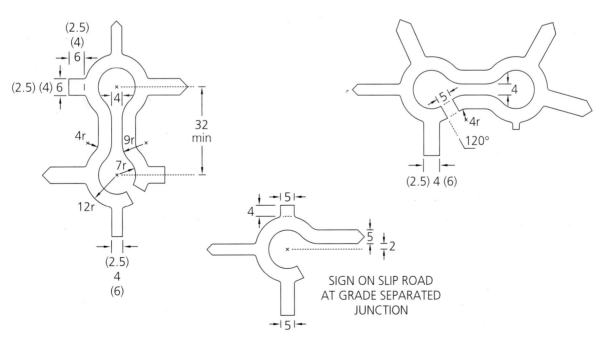

SIGN ON SLIP ROAD AT GRADE SEPARATED JUNCTION

Figure 5-32

5.54 On dual carriageways where there are no gaps in the central reservation, it may be necessary to make a U-turn at a roundabout in order to reach a particular destination. A special map type symbol may be used; the design of this is shown in figure 5-33. This sign would replace the standard map type advance direction sign for a roundabout junction (diagram 2022) and would include destinations not associated with the U-turn. As an alternative, a standard map type sign could be provided, with the U-turn destination shown on a separate stack type sign incorporating the special U-turn arrow as shown in diagram 2035 (see section 14). Where the U-turn is associated with a traffic regulation order, a sign to diagram 2010.1 should be used in conjunction with a separately sited sign to diagram 2022.

SYMBOLS (OTHER THAN TRIANGULAR WARNING SIGNS AND REGULATORY SIGN ROUNDELS) ON MAP TYPE SIGNS

5.55 Where symbols are placed alongside a tiled legend beneath a horizontal route arm, they should normally be positioned at the opposite end to the point of the route arm. *In the case of the "P" parking symbol, this will always be placed to the left of its associated legend unless it is being used in conjunction with a tourist attraction.* The special rules given in para 4.8 then apply. Where the aircraft symbol is used, this should generally be placed to the right of the airport name. The position of other symbols may be varied, but only where this would improve the overall appearance of the sign.

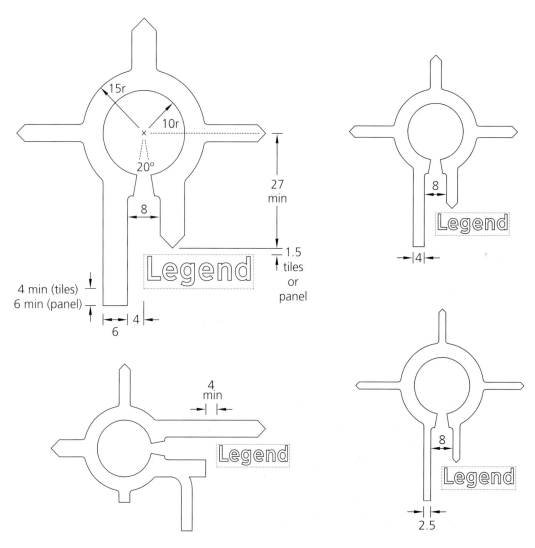

Figure 5-33

5.56 Symbols associated with route arms which are not horizontal should be positioned adjacent to any associated legend in a manner which produces the best sign layout. In most cases the symbol will be placed to the right of the legend. The "P" parking symbol and the aircraft symbol should be positioned as described in para 5.55.

5.57 Some symbols may be centred below the legend tiles. This is the case with the ferry symbol illustrated in diagrams 2007 and 2120. The lorry symbol when used on a black panel is always centred horizontally on any legend above. The panel will be ranged left with any other blocks associated with the same route symbol.

5.58 Those symbols which have a directional element to their design are listed at Appendix B and should face either left or right to accord with the general direction of the associated route arm. Where the route arm is vertical the symbol should face left. The aircraft symbol is normally rotated to point in the same direction as the route arm, except that the symbol should never point below the horizontal.

5.59 An example of the use of symbols on a map type sign is illustrated in figure 5-34.

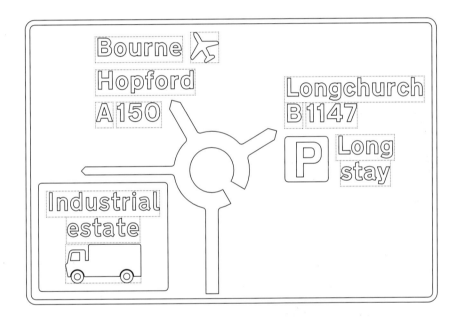

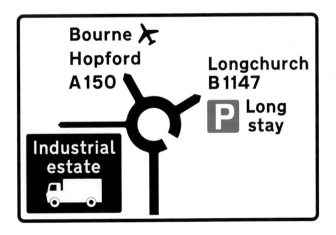

Figure 5-34

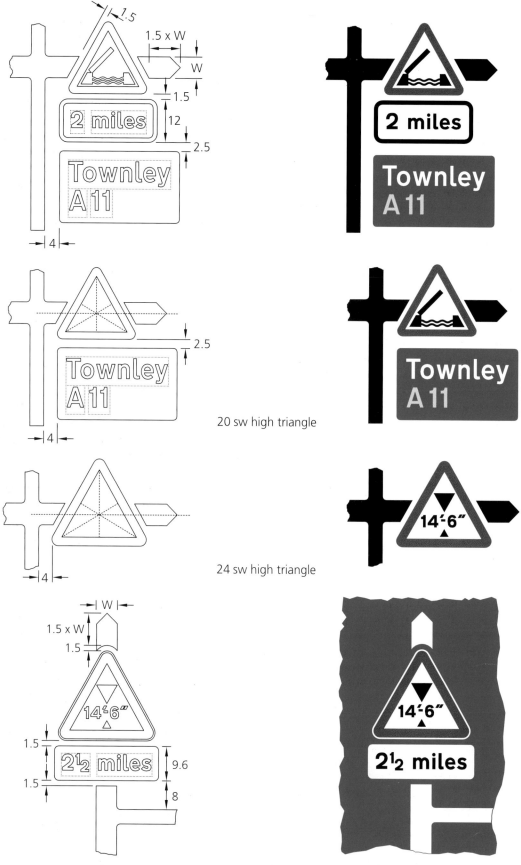

20 sw high triangle

24 sw high triangle

Distance plates are designed as normal signs and then reduced to 80% of their size.
All dimensions are in stroke widths based on the main x-height

Figure 5-35

TRIANGULAR WARNING SIGNS ON MAP TYPE SIGNS (HORIZONTAL AND VERTICAL ARMS)

5.60 Figure 5-35 shows how warning signs are added to the horizontal and vertical route arms of map type signs. Where the sign has a green, blue or brown background *a white edge is added to the outside of the triangle.*

5.61 The appropriate heights for the triangles (excluding any white edges) are given in Appendix D. The position of the triangle, as shown in figure 5-35, remains the same regardless of the triangle height and width of route symbol.

5.62 A warning sign may include a distance plate to diagram 572. This is designed as a normal sign and then reduced to 80% of its size. Where the border is omitted (i.e. white panel on a green, blue or brown background) the corner radii do not change. These remain at 1.5 sw based on the plate x-height (i.e. 1.2 sw based on the x-height of the main sign).

5.63 It may not always be possible to determine the length of the horizontal route arm in accordance with para 5.6. The dimensions shown will fix the minimum length of the arm. However, where the legend block has a long place name, the arm should be extended as appropriate. The horizontal position of the triangle may be adjusted in this case, provided the dimensions shown in figure 5-35 are treated as minimum values. The arm should not extend beyond the length of the legend block. Where this is likely to occur, the legend block should be moved away from the vertical route arm.

5.64 Where two triangular signs are used in order to indicate both imperial and metric height limits, the metric sign should always be placed to the right of the imperial sign. Where a distance plate is used on a vertical arm, it may not be possible to centre this below the two triangles (see figure 5-36). Where two triangular signs on the same route arm indicate different hazards, any distance plate should be associated with the appropriate sign. Where this would result in the two triangles being further apart than 6 sw, it is strongly recommended that the triangles be omitted from the sign and separate signing used to indicate the hazards.

5.65 The minimum distance between any triangle or plate and any sign border is 2.5 sw.

5.66 The minimum distance between the top of a triangle on the side arm and any unrelated legend above should be 14 sw for a panel, patch or symbol, 12.5 sw for a reduced x-height legend ("alternative route" etc, see para 3.37), and 12 sw for any legend at the main x-height. (See also para 5.67.)

5.67 The dimensions relating to the various gaps apply equally to plates with and without borders and to triangles with and without white edges. The gap is measured to the outside of any border or edge provided.

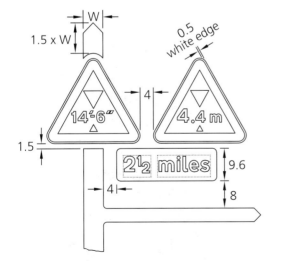

Distance plates are designed as normal signs and then reduced to 80% of their size.
All dimensions are in stroke widths based on the main x-height

Figure 5-36

REGULATORY SIGNS ON MAP TYPE SIGNS (HORIZONTAL AND VERTICAL ARMS)

5.68 Figure 5-37 illustrates the design of the sign shown in diagram 2108. In addition to the regulatory roundel, it demonstrates the use of the "alternative route" message. A plate indicating the distance from the junction to the restriction should always be used unless the restriction indicated commences at the junction. The gap of 2 sw immediately above the tip of the forward route arm is reduced to 0.5 sw when the arm is vertical or within 15° of the vertical (i.e. the gap is 0.5 sw greater than the standard gap - see paras 3.37, 5.3, 5.8, 5.10 and 5.73).

5.69 Regulatory signs with supplementary plates to diagrams 572, 618.1 or 953.2, or without such plates, may be added to vertical route arms in a manner similar to triangular warning signs. The design of the plates is the same as for those used with warning triangles (see para 5.62). Examples are illustrated in figure 5-38.

5.70 Where a regulatory sign with a red roundel is placed on a green, blue or brown background, a white edge 0.5 sw wide is added, similar to the white edge on the triangular warning sign. Certain regulatory signs such as "no entry" and "buses only" have white borders and therefore an additional white

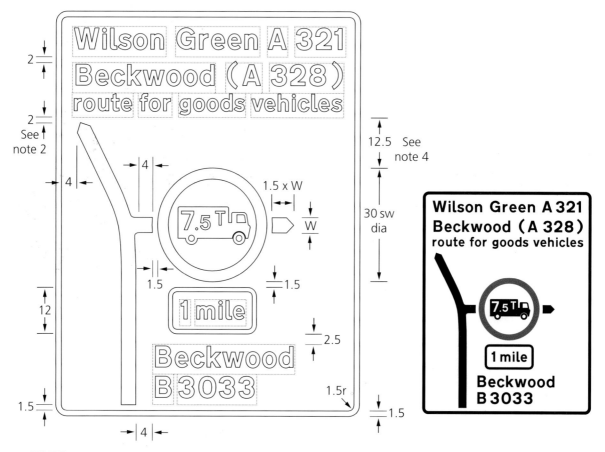

NOTES

1. "route for goods vehicles" is 80% of the main x-height.
2. This dimension is reduced to 0.5 sw when the route arm is vertical or within 15° of the vertical.
3. "1 mile" supplementary plate designed as a normal sign, but 80% of the size of the main sign x-height/stroke width (12 sw height shown is for main sign x-height - i.e. 0.8 x 15 sw).
4. This dimension is varied to 14 sw when measured to a panel, patch or symbol, and varied to 12 sw when measured to a tiled legend at the main x-height.
5. All dimensions are in stroke widths based on main x-height.

Figure 5-37 (diagram 2108)

edge is not required. When these particular regulatory signs are placed on a sign with a white background the white border becomes "invisible", and the 1.5 sw gap to the route symbol is measured to the edge of the red or blue part of the roundel. The effective roundel diameter in this instance is reduced to 96% of its normal size. Thus a 16 sw roundel becomes 15.36 sw and a 20 sw roundel becomes 19.2 sw (the red or blue part of the roundel is not increased or scaled to the nominal diameters of 16 sw or 20 sw).

5.71 As with triangular warning signs, it may not always be possible to determine the length of the horizontal route arm in accordance with para 5.6. The dimensions shown will fix the minimum length of the arm. However, where the legend block has a long place name, the arm should be extended as appropriate. The horizontal position of the roundel may be adjusted in this case, provided the dimensions shown in figure 5-37 are treated as minimum values. The arm should not extend beyond the length of the legend block. Where this is likely to occur, the legend block should be moved away from the vertical route arm.

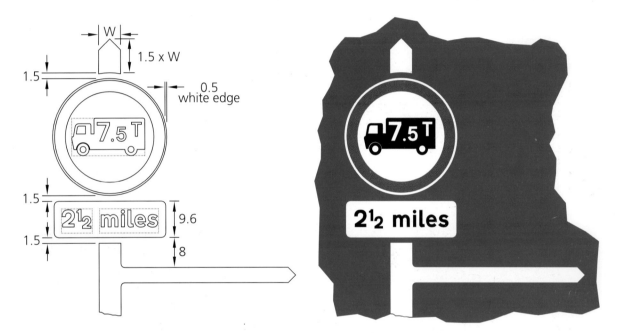

Distance plates are designed as normal signs and then reduced to 80% of their size.
All dimensions are in stroke widths based on the main x-height

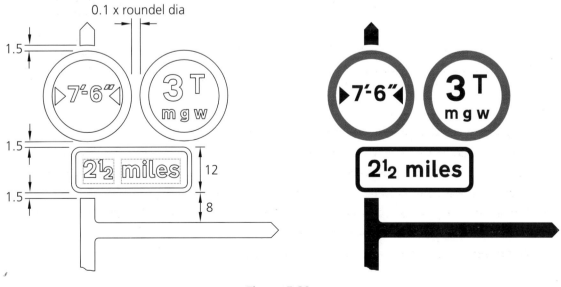

Figure 5-38

5.72 The diameter of the roundel, in stroke widths, varies according to the type of prohibition indicated. A list of roundel sizes is given in Appendix D.

5.73 The alternative route message shown in figure 5-37 has an x-height 80% of the main x-height. To compensate for the smaller tiles, any vertical space directly below the legend is increased by 0.5 sw, based on the main x-height. Thus the normal vertical space above the inclined route arm is increased from 1.5 sw to 2 sw (see para 3.37).

5.74 Where a "no right turn", "no left turn", "no entry" or "no vehicles" regulatory sign is used on a map type sign, the section of route arm beyond the roundel is omitted. The banned turn signs are always placed on the arm of the junction into which traffic may not turn, and not on the approach arm. The "no vehicles" regulatory roundel must always be used with a "No vehicles" supplementary plate which may include a distance, as shown in diagram 2009. The vertical space between the "No vehicles" legend and any distance is 2 sw, based on the x-height of the plate.

5.75 The minimum distance between any roundel or plate and any sign border is 2.5 sw.

5.76 The dimensions relating to the various gaps apply equally to plates with and without borders and to roundels with and without white edges. The gap is measured to the outside of any border or edge provided.

WARNING AND REGULATORY SIGNS ON MAP TYPE SIGNS (INCLINED ROUTE ARMS)

5.77 Figure 5-39 shows triangular warning signs added to route arms inclined at 30° above the horizontal. Where a distance plate is added, care has to be taken to shape the cut line through the arm. This will vary according to the length of the plate and the size of triangle. The cut-out radius of 4 sw (3 sw for a plate without a border) applies only where the arm intersects both the triangle and the plate. In other circumstances a curved cut-out in the arm will be offset by 1.5 sw from either the corner of the triangle or plate as appropriate.

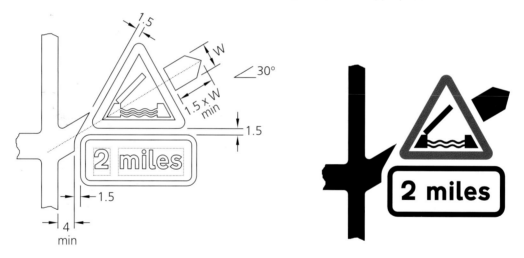

Distance plates are designed as normal signs and then reduced to 80% of their size.
All dimensions are in stroke widths based on the main x-height

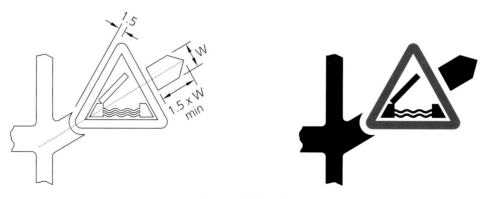

Figure 5-39

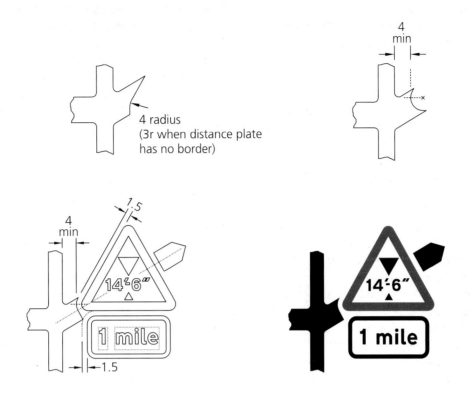

Distance plates are designed as normal signs and then reduced to 80% of their size.
All dimensions are in stroke widths based on the main x-height

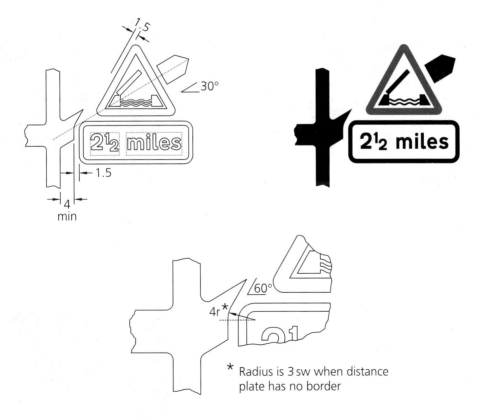

Figure 5-39 (continued)

5.78 Figures 5-40 and 5-41 show triangular warning signs added to route arms inclined at 45° and 60° above the horizontal respectively. Figure 5-42 shows other examples of inclined arms, including those with two triangles.

5.79 Single regulatory signs without plates will generally fit without complication into a route arm inclined at any angle. The roundel should be no closer than 4 sw to any vertical route arm. Figures 5-43 and 5-44 show various layouts for single and twin roundels with plates. In the case of the single roundel on a 30° arm, the plate should be placed as close to the roundel as possible without going below the minimum dimensions shown. Design details shown in figure 5-42 for the single triangular sign with the "2½ miles" plate also apply to roundels in a similar situation.

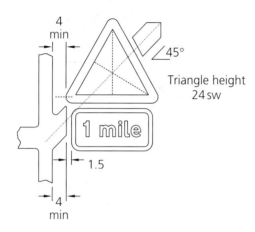

Distance plates are designed as normal signs and then reduced to 80% of their size. All dimensions are in stroke widths based on the main x-height

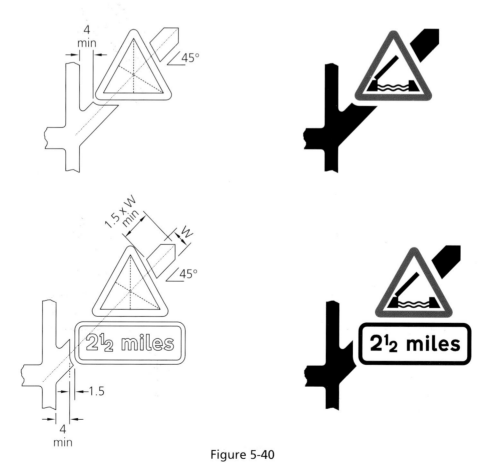

Figure 5-40

5.80 Figures 5-39 to 5-44 cover the most common situations of placing roundels and triangles on inclined arms. The design details shown should be used as appropriate in other situations. Some

flexibility may be required, the overriding consideration being that the final layout should produce a balanced design avoiding odd-shaped cut-outs in the route arms.

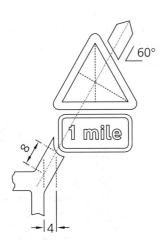

Distance plates are designed as normal signs and then reduced to 80% of their size. All dimensions are in stroke widths based on the main x-height

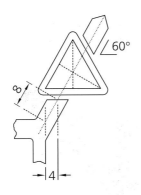

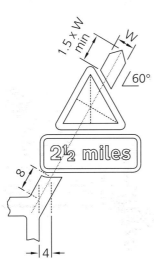

Figure 5-41

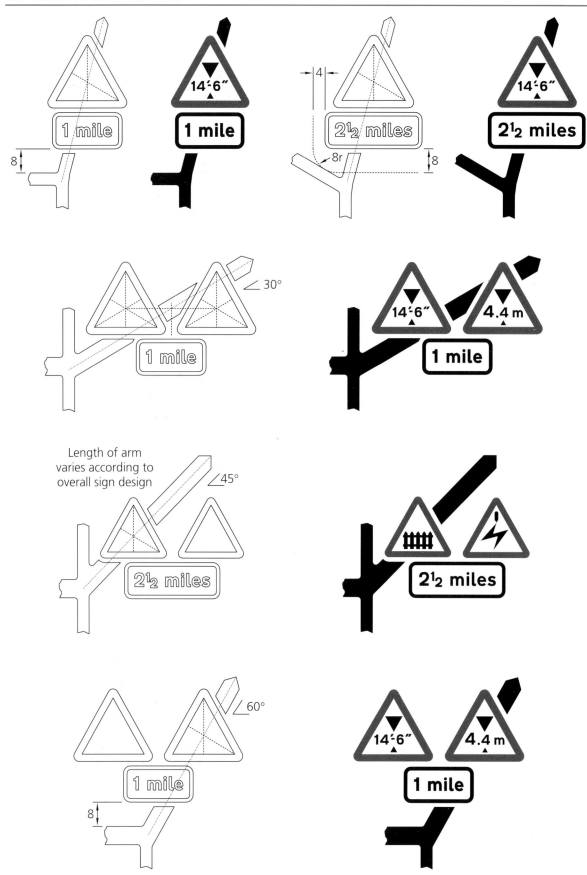

Distance plates are designed as normal signs and then reduced to 80% of their size.
All dimensions are in stroke widths based on the main x-height

Figure 5-42

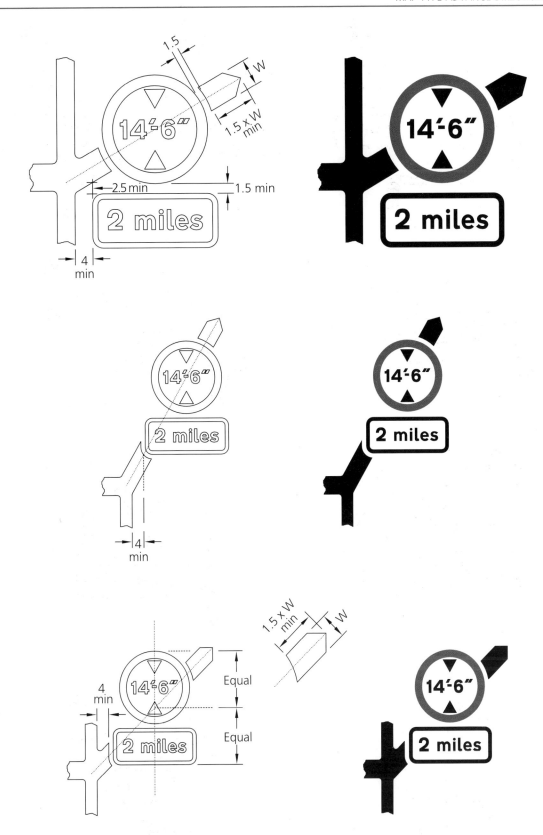

Distance plates are designed as normal signs and then reduced to 80% of their size.
All dimensions are in stroke widths based on the main x-height

Figure 5-43

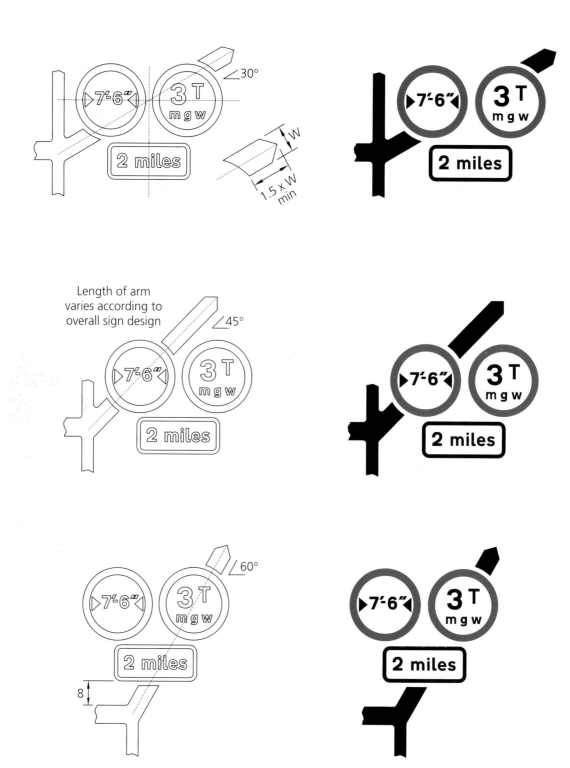

Distance plates are designed as normal signs and then reduced to 80% of their size.
All dimensions are in stroke widths based on the main x-height

Figure 5-44

REGULATORY AND TRIANGULAR WARNING SIGNS ASSOCIATED WITH THE SAME DESTINATION

5.81 There may be occasions when it is required to show both a regulatory and a triangular warning sign on the same destination panel. The horizontal space between the two signs is the same as for stack type signs, as shown in figure 4-17. The diameter of the roundel and the height of the triangle should both be the same, based on the size of the larger sign as listed in Appendix D. The positioning of the signs on the route arm symbol should be based on the design rules for two triangles or two roundels as shown in figures 5-36, 5-38, 5-42 and 5-44. When the route arm symbol is horizontal, the centre line of the arm should pass through the centre of the roundel and not the centroid of the triangle.

NO THROUGH ROAD SYMBOL ON MAP TYPE SIGNS

5.82 A red bar, similar to the one shown in diagram 817, may be added to a stub on a map type sign to indicate "no through road". The width of the stub should always be 2.5 sw, even though the route indicated may have a higher status (e.g. a short two-way section of road forming part of a one-way system). When the red bar is placed on a white background sign, a gap is provided between the bar and the stub. However, should the red bar be placed on a green, blue or brown background sign, the stub is extended to form a border around the bar. Figure 5-45 shows the detailed design of the red bar and stub.

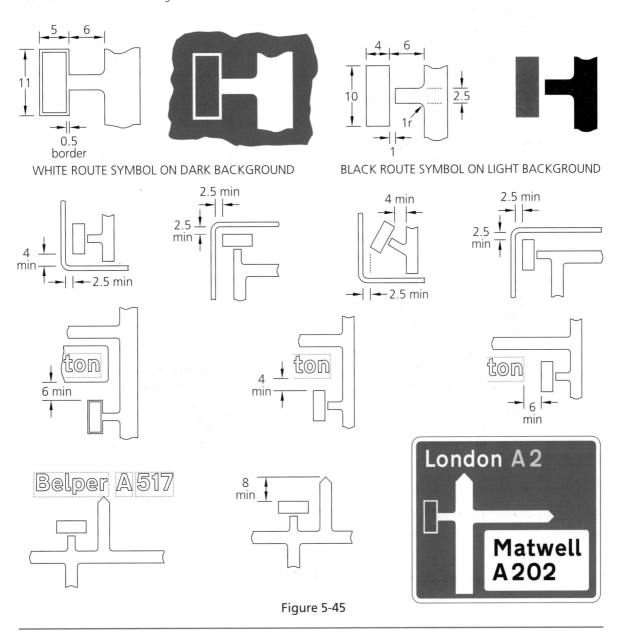

WHITE ROUTE SYMBOL ON DARK BACKGROUND

BLACK ROUTE SYMBOL ON LIGHT BACKGROUND

Figure 5-45

6 DEDICATED LANE ADVANCE DIRECTION SIGNS

GENERAL DESIGN RULES

6.1 Figure 6-1 shows the design of a sign for an at-grade junction where the right hand lane is for use by right turning traffic only. Such a sign may also be used on the exit slip road of a grade separated junction.

6.2 Figure 6-2 shows a main carriageway advance direction sign on the approach to a grade separated junction with a lane drop. Figure 6-3 is the final advance direction sign used at lane drop junctions. Details of the chevron markings in figure 6-3 are shown in figure 6-4.

6.3 For all signs covered in this section, the longer 18 sw arrow replaces the standard 16 sw length. The width of the arrow head remains at 8 sw. The tops of arrows are always aligned vertically. The curved arrow in figure 6-1 is reversed when indicating a left turn lane. Where two or more lanes lead to the same destination, a horizontal bar is used as shown. This also applies to multiple left and right turn lanes.

Where there is no bar, the gap between legend and arrow head is generally 1.5 sw for tiles and 2.5 sw for panels, patches and symbols. The gap may be increased to produce a balanced design (e.g. by aligning the destination blocks, as shown in figure 6-2). However, this increased gap is not recommended for signs with chevron markings (see figure 6-3) where this would increase the width of the sign.

6.4 The arrows, including any left or right turn arrows, are centred horizontally in their respective lanes (in the case of the curved arrow it is the full 14 sw width that is centred). This does not necessarily apply to the inclined arrow shown in figure 6-3, where the position is chosen to give a balanced appearance. Lanes leading to the same destination should have equal width. The widest lane on the sign should not be greater than twice the width of the narrowest lane. If necessary, the width of the narrow lanes should be increased and the legend centred accordingly. Any horizontal bar should extend to a point 2.5 sw from any vertical border or lane line.

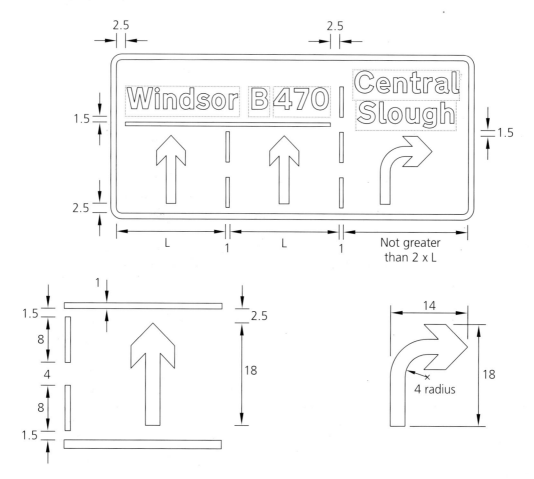

Figure 6-1

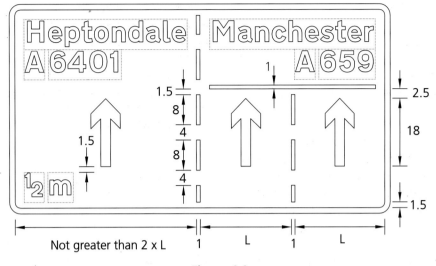

Figure 6-2

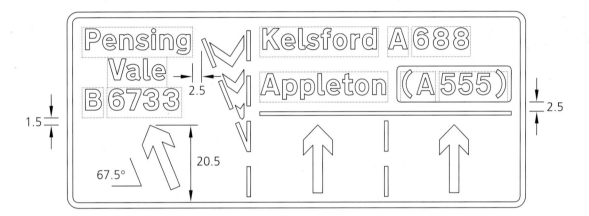

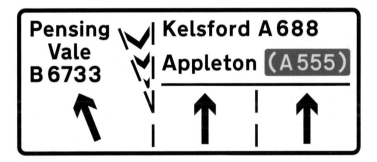

Figure 6-3

6.5 The lane lines are always positioned vertically so that the top of a line is 1 sw above the top of a vertical arrow head, whether the sign has horizontal bars or not.

6.6 Where a lane line is truncated at the top of the sign (as in figure 6-2) the minimum length of line should be 3 sw. Where this cannot be achieved, the line should be omitted, as shown in figure 6-1. The minimum gap between the lane line and the top border is 1.5 sw.

6.7 Where a sign incorporates the chevron markings shown in figure 6-4, it may be necessary to adjust the position of the chevrons if there are three or more lines of legend. Simply to extend the length of the chevron marking (and hence the number of chevrons) would unnecessarily increase the overall width of the sign. In most cases the solution is to move the chevron markings upwards by one lane line module of 12 sw, as illustrated in figure 6-5.

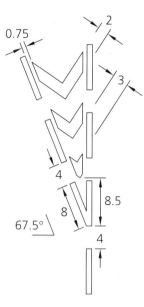

Figure 6-4

6.8 Route numbers on separate lines may be ranged right to emphasize that they are associated with right hand lanes, as shown in figure 6-2. However, individual destinations should always be ranged left as illustrated in figure 6-6.

6.9 The distance to the junction shown in figure 6-2 may be varied only to 1m, $^2/_3$m or $^1/_3$m. Any other distance will require special authorisation. Distances to destinations must not be included on dedicated lane signs.

6.10 A junction name may be added to the top of the signs (see paras 3.39 to 3.41). However, where there is more than one sign on the approach to the junction, the name should be added only to the first sign.

6.11 Symbols may be added to the signs in the same way that they are added to stack type and map type signs (see paras 6.12 to 6.14 for warning and regulatory signs on dedicated lane advance direction signs). Generally the symbol is placed to the right of the legend for left turn and ahead lanes, and to the left of the legend for right turn lanes. The symbol may be centred below the legend if this results in a more compact sign. *The "P" parking symbol is always placed to the left of its associated legend unless used in conjunction with a tourist attraction.* The special rules given in para 4.8 then apply. Where the aircraft symbol is used, this should

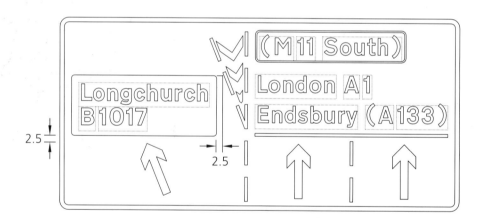

Figure 6-5

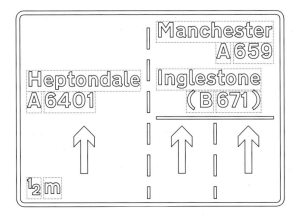

Figure 6-6

generally be placed to the right of the airport name. Where the airport name is the same as the place name destination along the same route, the aircraft symbol may be used on its own on a separate line ranged left. Symbols with a directional element (see Appendix B) should face either left or right as

appropriate. For ahead destinations, the symbol should face left, except for the aircraft symbol which should point vertically upwards. Where the arrow is inclined at 22.5° on the final advance direction sign at a grade separated junction, any aircraft symbol associated with that direction should also be inclined at 22.5° to the vertical. Examples of the use of symbols are given in figure 6-7.

WARNING AND REGULATORY SIGNS ON DEDICATED LANE ADVANCE DIRECTION SIGNS

6.12 The design rules are basically the same as those for stack type signs (see paras 4.16 to 4.27), except that the arrows are below the legend blocks. *A plate indicating the distance from the junction to the restriction should always be used with a regulatory sign unless the restriction indicated commences at the junction.* Distance plates may also be added below triangular warning signs.

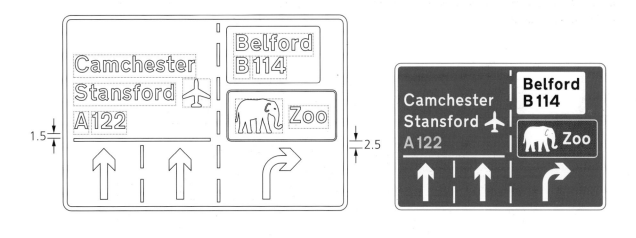

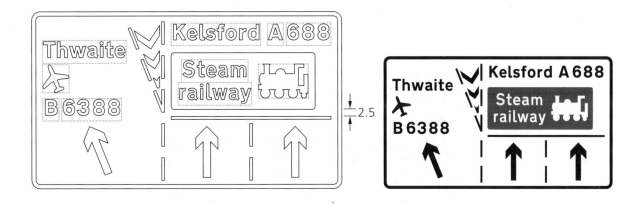

Figure 6-7

6.13 Any triangle or roundel should be placed to the left of the destination when the route indicated is either ahead or to the left. When the route is to the right, the triangle or roundel should be placed to the right of the destination. An example is shown in figure 6-8. It should be noted that the addition of a triangle or roundel to a single lane destination can make the sign extremely wide. In figure 6-8 it was necessary to increase the width of the two left hand lanes to ensure that the wide single lane is not greater than twice the width of the narrowest lane (see figure 6-2). The use of more than one triangle or roundel associated with the same destination is therefore not recommended.

6.14 The vertical distance between any triangle, roundel or plate and any arrow or horizontal bar below should be a minimum of 2.5 sw, as shown in figure 6-8.

6.15 Where the sign includes the "alternative route" legend, the design rules set out in paras 3.37 and 3.38 should be used.

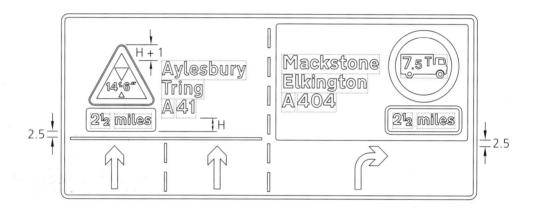

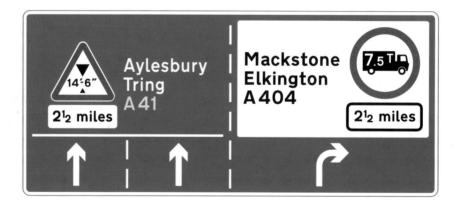

Distance plates are designed as normal signs and then reduced to 80% of their size.
All dimensions are in stroke widths based on the main x-height

Figure 6-8

FLAG TYPE DIRECTION SIGNS

7.1 The background colour of the sign must be appropriate to the status of the route indicated. Tourist panels and route number patches, *but not blue, green or white destination panels*, may be added to flag type signs. The design of blue background signs indicating the start of a motorway or motorway slip road is covered in paras 10.5 to 10.9. Signs indicating tourist attractions only should have a brown background. Signs indicating lorry routes should have a black background, signs indicating cycle routes should have a blue background and signs which indicate MoD establishments should have a white background with a red border and chevron.

7.2 Figure 7-1 shows the basic design of flag type signs. The width of the chevron is determined from the overall height of the sign and should be in accordance with the table. Vertical positioning and layout of the legend is the same as for stack type signs (see section 4 for stack type signs and section 3 for general rules).

7.3 No part of any legend should cross a line offset from the chevron by 2 sw. With some designs it may be possible to tuck the legend into the chevron, as shown in figure 7-1. However, where two signs are mounted back to back they need to be the same length. This can be achieved by not tucking the legend into the chevron.

7.4 The rules relating to distances are described in paras 3.32 to 3.35.

The appropriate vertical spacing between "Linscombe Bay" and the tourist attraction panel is 2.5 sw (block spacing) (see para 3.25)

Legend block (tiles, square corners of panels or patches, and symbols) shall not cross this line.

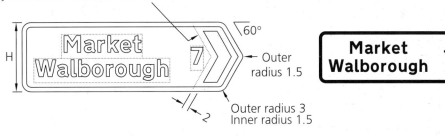

HEIGHT OF SIGN H sw	WIDTH OF CHEVRON W sw
< 19	3
19 to < 27	4
27 to < 35	5
35 to < 43	6
43 to < 51	7
51 to < 59	8

Where the height exceeds 59 sw it is recommended that two or more smaller signs are used

Figure 7-1

7.5 The design rules for positioning symbols on direction signs are generally the same as for other signs, as shown in figure 3-9 (see paras 7.6 to 7.10 for warning and regulatory signs on flag type signs). Generally the symbol should be placed at the opposite end to the chevron. The symbol may be centred below the legend if this results in a more compact sign. *The "P" parking symbol is always placed to the left of its associated legend unless used in conjunction with a tourist attraction.* The special rules given in para 4.8 then apply. Where the aircraft symbol is used, this should generally be placed to the right of the airport name, whether the sign points to the left or to the right. Where the airport name is the same as the place name destination along the same route, the aircraft symbol may be used on its own on a separate line ranged left. Symbols with a directional element (see

Appendix B) should face either left or right as appropriate. The aircraft symbol should always be horizontal, pointing left or right as appropriate. Examples of the use of symbols are given in figure 7-2.

WARNING AND REGULATORY SIGNS ON FLAG TYPE SIGNS

7.6 The design rules for placing triangles and roundels adjacent to chevrons on flag type signs are shown in figure 7-3. The triangle or roundel is always placed on the same side of the legend as the chevron. Where the sign has a green or brown background *a white edge is added to the outside of the triangle or roundel.* The appropriate heights for the triangles or roundels (excluding any white edges) are given in Appendix D.

7.7 Distance plates to diagram 572 may be added below the triangles or roundels, as shown in figure 7-3. The plate is designed as a normal sign and then reduced to 80% of its size. Thus if the x-height of the main sign is 100 mm, the x-height of the plate will be 80 mm. Where the plate is placed on a green or brown background the border is omitted, the corner radii remaining at 1.5 sw based on the plate x-height (i.e. 1.2 sw based on the x-height of the main sign). The plate should not cross a line offset from the chevron by 2 sw. *A plate indicating the distance from the junction to the restriction should always be used unless the restriction indicated commences at the junction.*

7.8 Where a destination is indicated to the right, any distance is generally placed to the right of the warning or regulatory sign. However, where more than one destination is shown, the clarity of the sign is improved, as for stack type advance direction signs, by placing the distances between the place names and the warning triangle or regulatory roundel (see figures 4-12 and 4-15 for stack type sign examples).

7.9 Two triangles or roundels, or one of each, may be included on a flag type sign. The design details are similar to those for stack type advance direction signs (see figures 4-13, 4-16 and 4-17).

7.10 The dimensions relating to the various gaps apply equally to plates with and without borders and to triangles with and without white edges. The gap is measured to the outside of any border or edge provided.

Figure 7-2

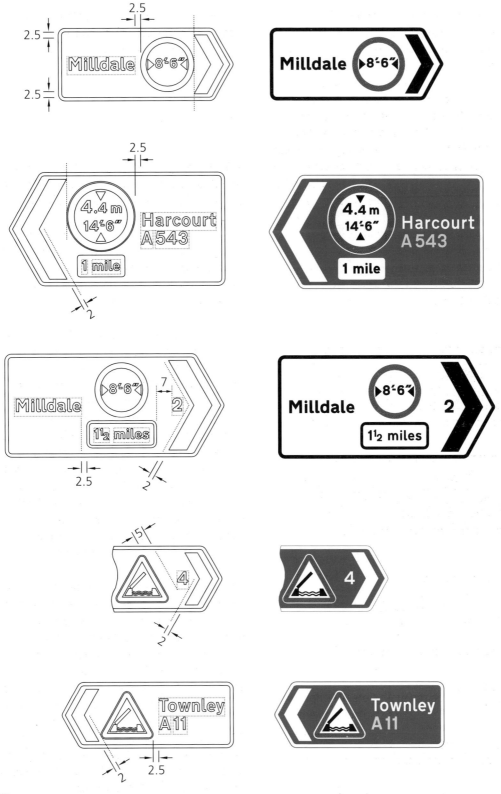

NOTES

1. The distance plates have an x-height equal to 80% of the main x-height and are designed in accordance with the normal design rules appropriate to the reduced x-height. Where a plate has an increased width (e.g. 2 miles) it should not cross the line shown offset from the chevron by 2 sw.

2. Dimensions shown are in stroke widths based on the main x-height.

Figure 7-3

RECTANGULAR DIRECTION SIGNS

7.11 The design of these signs is basically the same as for advance direction stack type signs. The ahead arrow, however, should be placed to the right of the destinations when traffic passes to the right of the sign to follow the route indicated. The sign should be located on the nose dividing the routes indicated.

7.12 At grade separated junctions the direction signs on the nose of the exit slip roads should show route numbers only. The arrow should be inclined at 22.5° to the vertical. Examples are shown in figure 7-4.

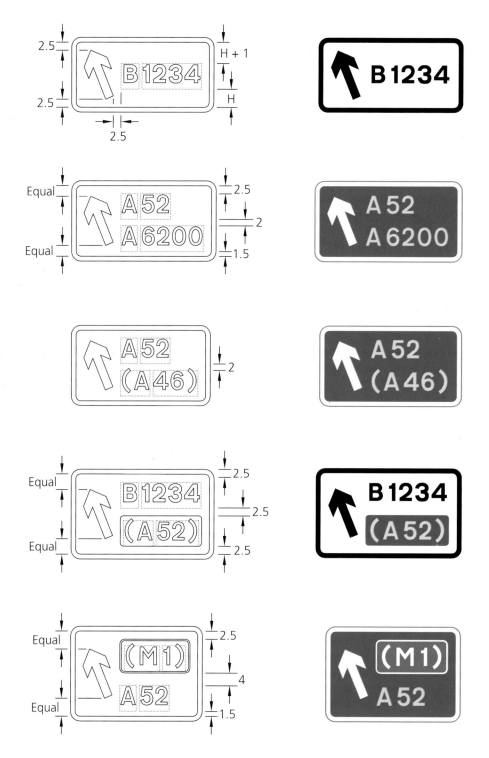

Figure 7-4

TRADITIONAL FINGERPOSTS

7.13 The traditional fingerpost design as shown in figure 7-5 should be used only on unnumbered rural roads where traffic speeds are low (see para 3.3).

7.14 The sign uses Transport Heavy capital letters, with an x-height between 40 mm and 60 mm. Lower case letters with an initial capital may be used as an alternative, but not on a sign that has other place names all in capitals. Where lower case letters are used, the recommended minimum x-height is 50 mm. The letters are always black on a white background. Signs using letter styles to replicate pre-1960s fingerposts may be specially authorised on request.

7.15 The sign, illustrated in diagram 2141, may be based on the flag type direction sign without the border and chevron, or may be square ended. Where the sign has a pointed end it is recommended that the angle should be between 120° and 90°. The corners of the sign may be either radiused or square. The legend may be either flush with the sign plate or raised above the surface of the plate. A narrow black border may be added to the sign.

7.16 The sign should generally be mounted on a single post at the appropriate end of the plate. This is particularly important where the "pointing" end of the sign is square. A finial may be added to the post.

7.17 Ideally all fingerpost signs on minor roads in a particular area should be to the same design, and traffic authorities are recommended to adopt a single consistent style throughout, matching wherever possible any surviving pre-war examples.

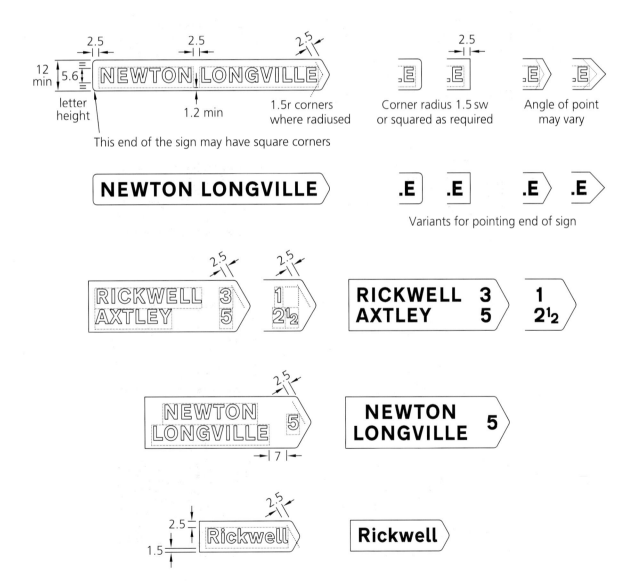

Figure 7-5

ROUTE CONFIRMATORY SIGNS INDICATING A SINGLE ROUTE

8.1 The design of route confirmatory signs for various combinations of tiles and patches is shown in figure 8-1. Design rules relating to the use of distances are covered in paras 3.32 to 3.35.

Regional destinations (see Appendix B of LTN 1/94) are centred horizontally on the sign and may overlap a distance tile on the line below.

8.2 Where destinations are reached by turning onto another route, they are shown unbracketed along with other destinations in mileage order.

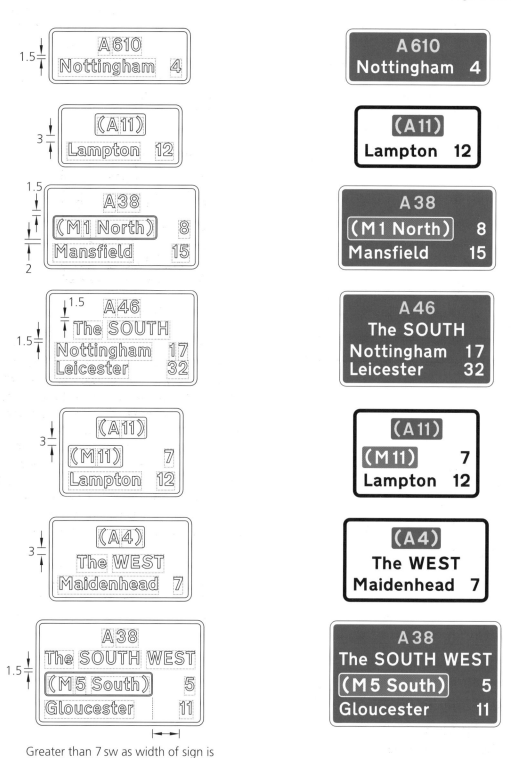

Greater than 7 sw as width of sign is determined by the regional destination

Figure 8-1

8.3 Regional destinations are always in capital letters (other than "The"). London is no longer treated as being a regional destination and should be included in the list of place name destinations in lower case letters and in mileage order (London will usually be the furthest place signed and therefore be on the bottom line).

8.4 The aircraft symbol may be used alongside and to the right of an airport name in accordance with the general rules on the positioning of symbols. The symbol should be vertical, with gaps to any line above or below being the same as for a route number patch. Where the airport name is the same as a place name destination on the sign, the aircraft symbol may be used on its own on a separate line only if it is quite clear which airport is being signed. Examples are shown in figure 8-2.

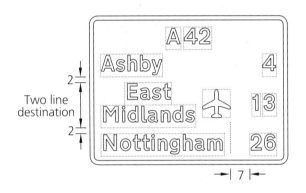

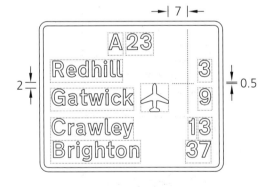

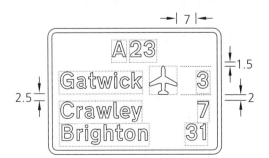

Figure 8-2

ROUTE CONFIRMATORY SIGNS INDICATING TWO ROUTES

8.5 Where destinations are reached by turning onto another route they can be listed separately, as shown in figure 8-3. This type of sign would be used where the junction is reached before the next destination on the existing route. In the case of a primary route sign which includes local destinations, the sign would be used where the junction is reached before the next primary destination. Where a primary destination on the present route is reached before the junction, a sign with a single route number, as shown in figure 8-1, is more appropriate.

Figure 8-3

8.6 The second route number may be placed at the top of the sign, as shown in the example "B 4040 (A 41)" (see figure 8-4). This is appropriate when all destinations on the sign are located on the bracketed route. However, for economy of space, this sign may also be used in the circumstances described in para 8.5, although no indication is given as to which route applies to which destination. In the example, "Potten End" and "Gaddesden" could well be local destinations on the B 4040 which then joins the A 41 leading to "Aylesbury". Signs of this design are helpful to drivers navigating by route numbers.

8.7 The appropriate spacings for various combinations of tiles and patches are shown in figure 8-4. Other dimensions and design rules are as described in paras 8.1, 8.3 and 8.4.

8.8 Route numbers are centred horizontally on the signs. Where two route numbers are side by side, the line may be longer than the destination lines. In such cases, the route numbers will determine the width of the sign. The destination lines should be lengthened accordingly by increasing the gaps between the place names and the distances.

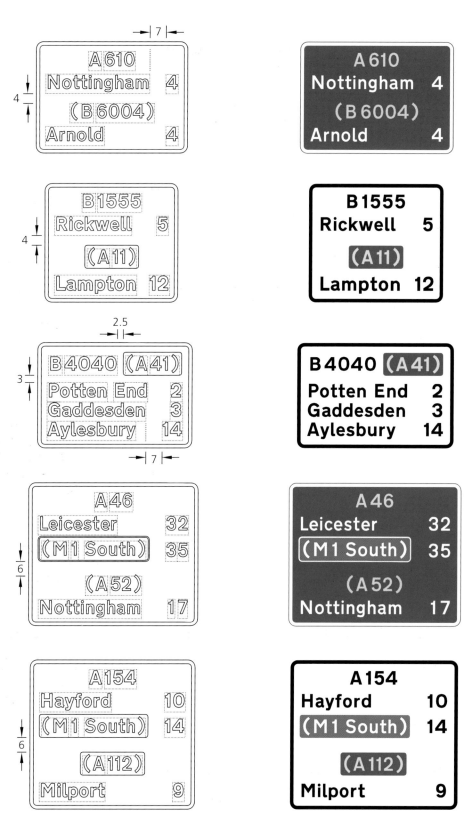

Figure 8-4

9 GANTRY MOUNTED SIGNS ON ALL-PURPOSE ROADS

9.1 There are two designs of gantry signs: one for non lane drop junctions and one for lane drop junctions (see para 3.2). Both are shown in figure 9-1.

The design of the downward pointing arrow used on the lane drop sign is shown in figure 9-2.

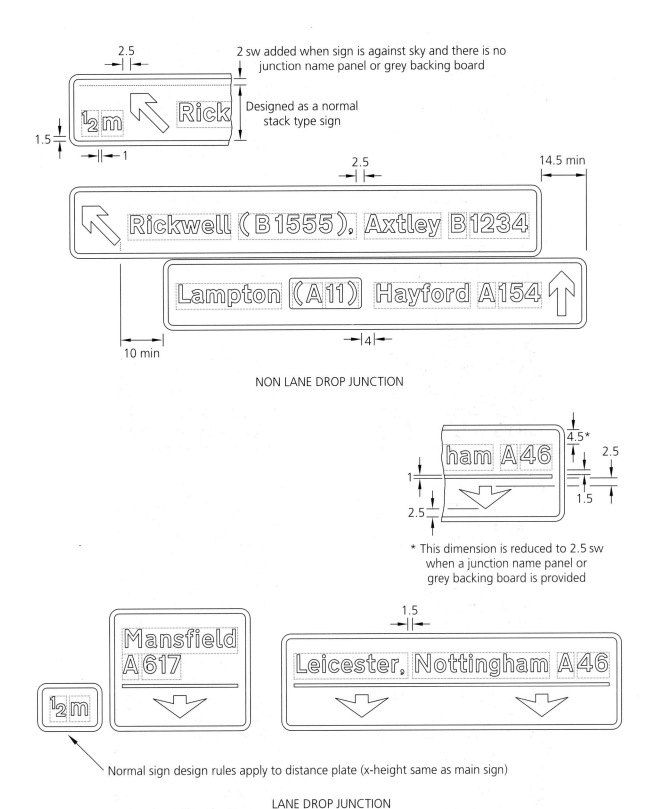

NON LANE DROP JUNCTION

* This dimension is reduced to 2.5 sw when a junction name panel or grey backing board is provided

Normal sign design rules apply to distance plate (x-height same as main sign)

LANE DROP JUNCTION

Figure 9-1

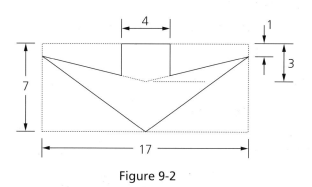

Figure 9-2

9.2 Both types of sign can include more than one destination on the same line. A comma is used to separate two place names in the same block (e.g. Leicester, Nottingham). A comma is also used where there are two blocks on the same line (e.g. Rickwell (B1555), Axtley B1234). Note that the horizontal gap is increased for block spacing. Where the first block ends with a patched route number a comma is not used, but the horizontal gap is increased to 4 sw.

9.3 The non lane drop sign is similar in design to a stack type sign with regard to the positioning of the arrows. The assembly comprises two signs, one above the other. The lower sign should normally be centred over the main carriageway. The upper sign is offset to the left by the dimensions shown, so that the inclined arrow is not directly above the lower sign. Where the upper sign is much longer than the lower sign, the assembly should be arranged so that the arrow on the lower sign is not directly below the upper sign. In some cases it may be necessary to shorten the upper sign by stacking the destinations vertically. Where the main carriageway bends to the right, both arrows may be turned through 22.5° in a clockwise direction (the angle between the two arrows remaining at 45°). The length of the arrow is generally 16 sw, but this is reduced to 14 sw for a vertical arrow alongside a single line legend. The distance to the junction may be added as shown.

9.4 The downward pointing arrows on the lane drop sign should be centred over the traffic lanes to which they apply. In some cases it may be necessary to extend the width of the sign to cover the appropriate lanes. When this is done, the horizontal spacing rules do not change, except that the gaps to the side borders are increased (the legend being centred horizontally on the sign). The horizontal bar is always positioned 2.5 sw from each side border (i.e. it may extend beyond the legend above). An example is shown in figure 9-3. The sign should cover at least three-quarters of the width of any lane to which it applies. Where the legend is in a panel (see para 9.9 and figure 9-5) the panel is *not* extended when the width of the main sign is extended. Where a single lane is indicated, the width of the sign may be greater than the lane width. In this case the sign may extend over part of the adjoining lane, but by no more than a quarter of a lane width. The sign may also be extended over any adjoining hard strip or verge. Abbreviated place names may be used to reduce the width of the sign. Any reduction in x-height in order to produce a smaller sign is strongly deprecated, because service to drivers is then markedly reduced. This can have significant road safety implications, and causes particular problems to older drivers, who tend to have slower reactions and less acute eyesight.

9.5 The distance to the junction may be added to a lane drop sign, as shown in figure 9-1.

9.6 Both types of sign may include a junction name panel at the top of the assembly. This should appear only on the first sign on the approach to the junction and would normally include the distance to the junction. Examples are shown in figure 9-4.

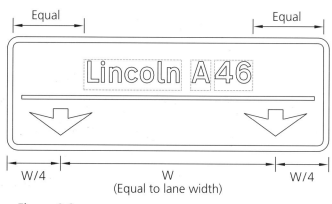

Figure 9-3

2 sw added when sign is against sky and there is no grey backing board

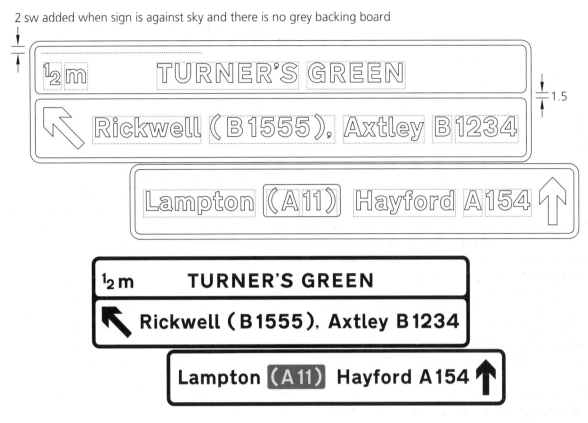

NON LANE DROP JUNCTION

2 sw added when sign is against sky and there is no grey backing board

Optional grey backing board

LANE DROP JUNCTION

Figure 9-4

2 sw added when sign is against sky and there is no junction name panel or grey backing board

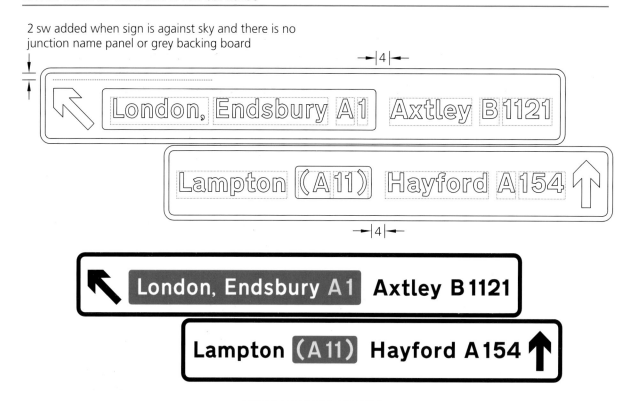

NON LANE DROP JUNCTION

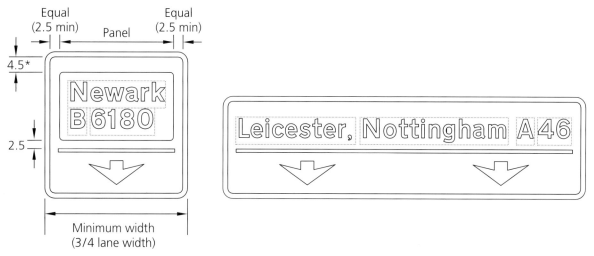

Equal (2.5 min)   Panel   Equal (2.5 min)

4.5*

2.5

Minimum width (3/4 lane width)

* This dimension is reduced to 2.5 sw when a junction name panel or grey backing board is provided

LANE DROP JUNCTION

Figure 9-5

9.7 The last point at which a driver can read the lower part of an overhead sign is described by a sight line from the bottom of the sign inclined at 10° below the horizontal. The sign should be mounted so that no part of the gantry structure, including any luminaires, obstructs this sight line.

9.8 Where the sign assembly is set against an open sky, when viewed from any point between the minimum clear visibility distance and the 10° sight line referred to in para 9.7, an extra 2 sw height is added to the top of the sign without adjusting the position of the legend or arrows (see figure 9-1). This provision is not necessary when there is a grey backing board at the top of the sign. Where a junction name is provided, the 2 sw adjustment is made to that part of the sign, as shown in figure 9-4.

9.9 The only panels which may be used on gantry signs are the green, white or blue panels indicating a route of a different status. Figure 9-5 shows the design details for the inclusion of these panels on gantry mounted signs.

9.10 On a primary route, where the exit slip road leads directly to a non-primary route only, a white panel is used for the non-primary destination block. Where the slip road leads directly to both a primary and a non-primary route, a white panel is *not* used.

9.11 On a non-primary route where the exit slip road leads directly to both a primary route and a non-primary route, the primary destination block is shown in a green panel.

9.12 The Regulations do not permit the inclusion of the following on gantry mounted directional signs:

    (i) warning signs

    (ii) regulatory signs

    (iii) distances to destinations

    (iv) panels indicating tourist attractions, lorry routes, MoD establishments and cycle routes.

MOTORWAY PANELS AND JUNCTION NUMBERS

10.1 Figure 10-1 shows the various designs of motorway panels used on advance direction signs on all-purpose roads. *Motorway panels are used only where the route indicated has motorway status.* A blue motorway route number patch should be used where the motorway is reached by an all-purpose road leading from the junction.

10.2 The background colour of a motorway panel is blue. A white border is added when the panel is placed on a green background sign (see para 3.14). The panel must include the motorway symbol as detailed on working drawing S 55. *The motorway number is in the Transport Medium alphabet and not the enlarged Motorway alphabet.* The addition of the junction number is optional. Distances to destinations should not be included on a blue motorway panel.

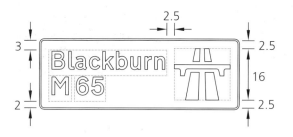

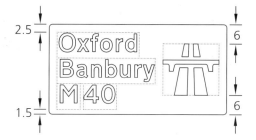

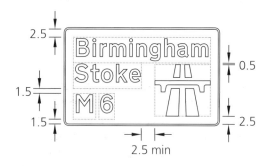

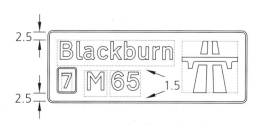

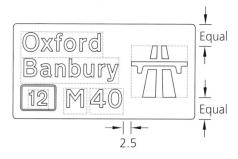

All dimensions are in stroke widths based on the main x-height

Figure 10-1

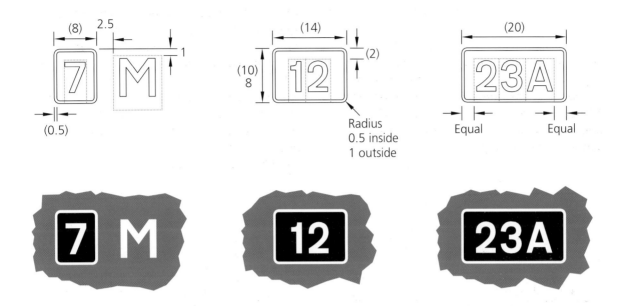

Unbracketed dimensions are in stroke widths based on x-height of main sign. Bracketed dimensions are in stroke widths based on x-height of junction number which is 80% of main x-height.

Figure 10-2

10.3 Where the motorway panel contains three or more lines of legend, it may be possible to tuck in the motorway symbol beneath the upper lines of legend; otherwise the symbol should be placed alongside the legend and centred vertically on the panel.

10.4 The design of the junction number patch is the same as that used on an advance direction sign on the main carriageway of a motorway. The junction number is white on a black background, and the patch has a white border. The characters are from the Transport Medium alphabet. *The x-height of the junction number is 80% of the x-height of the main sign (this also applies to signs on the main carriageways of motorways).* The design of the junction number patch is shown in figure 10-2. There are three fixed widths according to the number of characters making up the junction number. The junction number patch is aligned vertically so that the characters are centred on the characters (not tiles) of the motorway number.

DIRECTION SIGNS INDICATING ROUTES WITH MOTORWAY STATUS

10.5 Figure 10-3 shows the most common designs of direction signs indicating the start of a motorway or motorway slip road. They are located at major/minor priority junctions and at exits from roundabouts. Distances to destinations must not be included on these signs. The rectangular signs shown in figure 10-4 are for use at free flow grade separated junctions. They are situated on the nose of a motorway slip road leaving the main carriageway of an all-purpose road. Rectangular direction signs should not normally include any destinations. However, a compass point may be added to the motorway number. Compass points may also be added to flag type signs. Examples are shown in figure 10-5. The compass point tile includes brackets and additional space on the left hand side to ensure correct spacing. Flag type and rectangular signs must be used only where the sign points along a route which has motorway status.

10.6 The signs must include the motorway symbol as detailed on working drawing S 55. The motorway number is in the enlarged Motorway alphabet. Where full size brackets are used, the gap from the tiles to the top or bottom border is increased from 2.5 sw to 4 sw. This does not apply to the smaller compass point brackets as shown in figure 10-5. The addition of the junction number is optional. Where used, the junction number patch is aligned vertically with the motorway number alongside, as shown in figure 10-3. The design of the junction number patch is as detailed in para 10.4 and figure 10-2.

10.7 The motorway symbol has a height of 16 sw and should be positioned at least 2.5 sw from any border. Figure 10-3 shows that it may be possible to tuck in the symbol on a flag type sign that has three or more lines of legend. The symbol is always positioned at the opposite end to the chevron.

10.8 Motorway flag type signs with blue backgrounds may be used to direct traffic around a large roundabout or gyratory system where an exit has motorway status. These signs should be designed as conventional flag type signs (see section 7), without the motorway symbol, and with the motorway number in the *Transport Medium*

alphabet. This is because the actual route indicated (the roundabout etc) does not have motorway status. A junction number may be added and should be positioned in accordance with figures 10-1 and 10-2. Distances to destinations must not be included on these signs. The advance direction signs on the approach to the roundabout or gyratory system will, however, show the full motorway panel with the motorway symbol when indicating the motorway exit from the roundabout or gyratory.

10.9 Other design rules detailed in paras 7.2 and 7.3 apply to all motorway flag type signs.

All dimensions are in stroke widths based on the main x-height

Figure 10-3

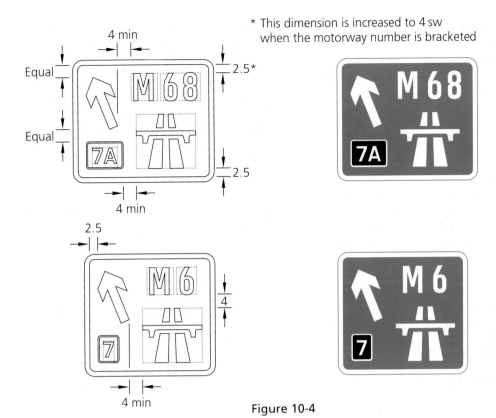

Figure 10-4

GENERAL DESIGN RULES FOR SIGNS ON MOTORWAYS

10.10 Signs on motorways generally follow the same design rules as those for signs on all-purpose roads. Thus a map type grade separated junction sign would be similar in design to the signs shown in figure 5-11 (e.g. the width of the route symbol is 5 sw). Gantry signs are similar to those in figure 9-1, except that the downward pointing arrows and horizontal bars are omitted from the lane drop signs (diagrams 2908.1 and 2909). The arrows on these signs are placed on blue patches located below the main sign assembly. The sign shown in diagram 2908.1 comprises the top part of the non lane drop sign mounted above a lane drop sign. This sign is used where a lane drop exit slip road closely follows a lane diverge. *Motorway signs do not have junction names* and, other than diagrams 2914 and 2914.1, *signs on the main carriageway never have coloured panels*. Distances to destinations are not shown on motorway signs, other than on route confirmatory signs.

10.11 Motorway signs differ from all-purpose road signs in that they use the Motorway alphabet for route numbers (except as detailed in paras 10.8, 10.15, 10.16 and 10.17). Spacing rules for the Motorway alphabet are shown in figure 10-6. It should be noted that, for vertical alignment, the

Motorway alphabet is treated in the same way as a panel, patch or symbol when placed alongside a destination in the Transport Medium alphabet. The Motorway tiles are positioned level with the Transport Medium tiles and then raised by 0.5 sw. Not only does this produce a balanced appearance, it ensures that for a single line legend the Motorway characters are centred vertically between the top and bottom borders of a gantry sign. Characters from the Motorway alphabet should be at least 2.5 sw from the arrow or horizontal bar in diagrams 2904 and 2904.1 or from any border. Where full size brackets (not compass point brackets) are used, the vertical gap to arrows, bars or borders should be at least 4 sw.

10.12 Special rules apply for vertical block spacing. Where the place name and route number are on the same line in each block, the vertical block spacing is 4 sw. However, this dimension is increased where the lower block has the place name and route number on different lines. As line spacing is set at 2 sw, it is important that the place name and route number are seen to be in the same block. The increased block spacing is 5 sw measured from the route number in the upper block, or 4.5 sw measured from the place name in the upper block, as appropriate. Where the lower block does not have an associated route number (e.g. "Services") the same increased block spacing rules apply.

93

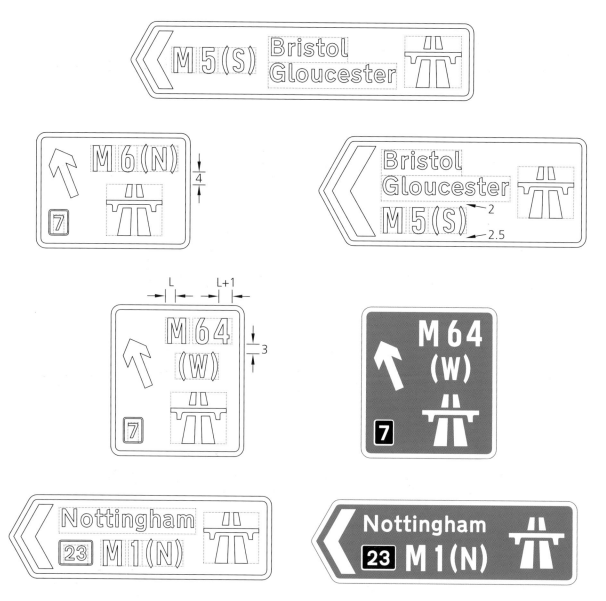

Figure 10-5

10.13 Where destinations are indicated to the left on gantry mounted signs (upper panel on diagrams 2908 and 2908.1, and panel over left hand lanes on diagram 2908.1 and 2909) the route number is placed to the left of the associated place name (see Bedford and Ampthill example in figure 10-6).

10.14 Figure 10-7 shows spacings appropriate to the design of map type signs. *The junction number should normally appear in the bottom left hand corner of the sign*. Exceptionally, it may be placed in the top left hand corner (see para 11.15). Figure 10-8 shows the arrangement for two separate exits being shown on the same sign where two junctions are very close together. Both side arms should be the same length, and, where possible, all destination blocks should be ranged left. Where a block ranged left would be spaced more than 4 sw horizontally from its associated route arm, the block may be moved to the right to ensure that it is still associated with the arm. It should be noted that this type of sign must not be modified by the addition of a forward destination and used as a final advance direction sign. The final advance direction sign at the first junction should be to the standard design shown in diagram 2906, with the second exit destinations being included with the forward destinations. The junction number for the first exit only should appear on this sign and should be placed in the bottom left hand corner.

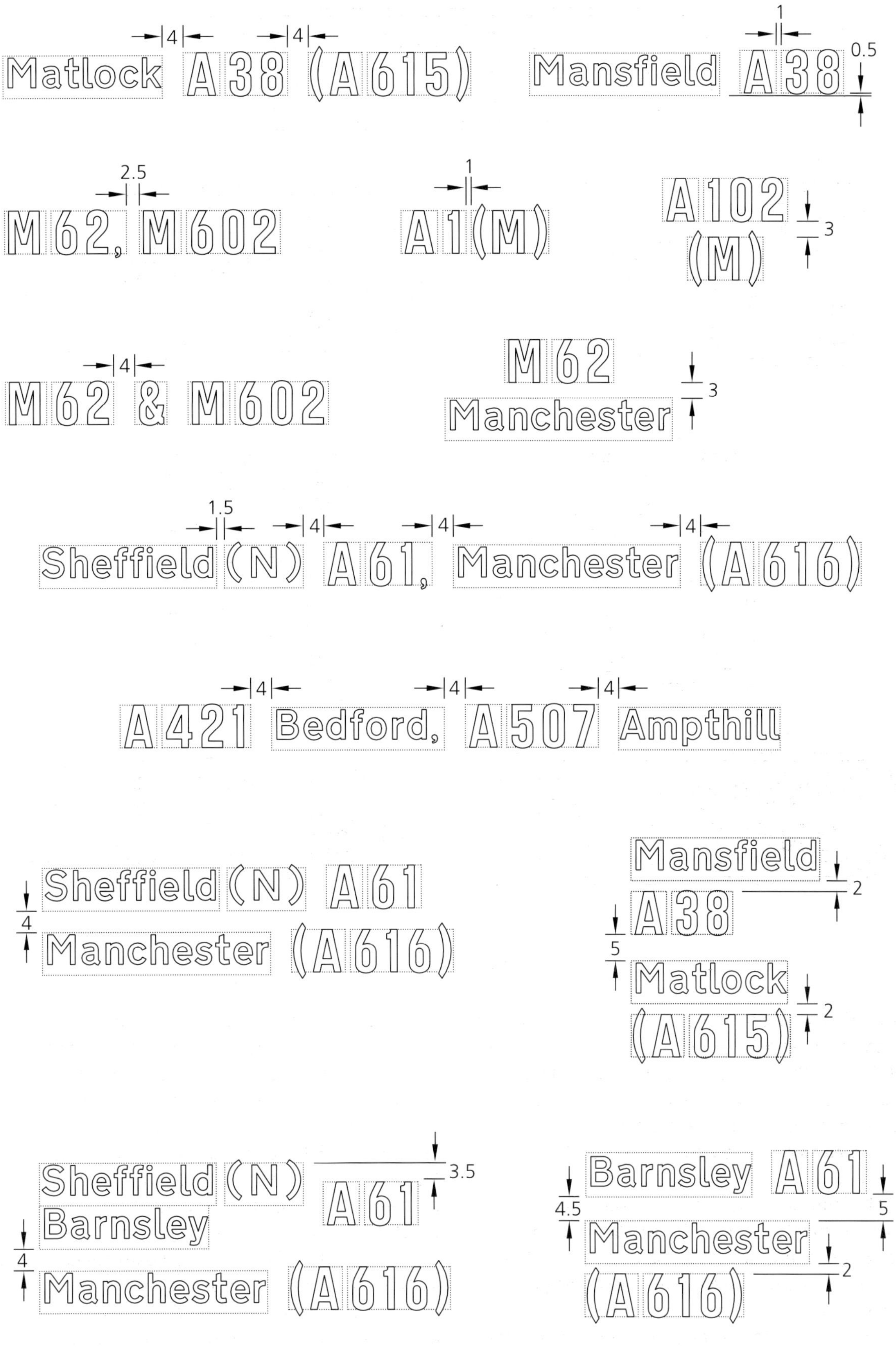

Matlock A38 (A615)

Mansfield A38

M62, M602

A1(M)

A102 (M)

M62 & M602

M62 Manchester

Sheffield (N) A61, Manchester (A616)

A421 Bedford, A507 Ampthill

Sheffield (N) A61 Manchester (A616)

Mansfield A38 Matlock (A615)

Sheffield (N) Barnsley A61 Manchester (A616)

Barnsley A61 Manchester (A616)

Figure 10-6

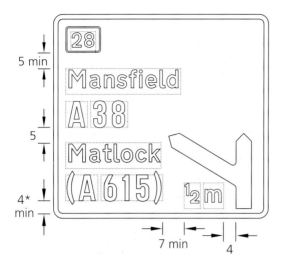

* This dimension is reduced to 2.5 sw min
  when the route number is unbracketed

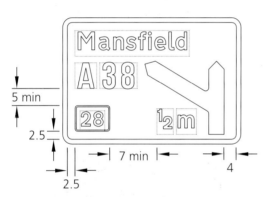

Figure 10-7

10.15 Advance direction signs on exit slip roads, other than diagram 2913.1, and the map type terminal roundabout sign on the main carriageway shown in diagram 2914 do not use the Motorway alphabet because destinations on the all-purpose routes are shown in panels of the appropriate colour and hence the Transport alphabet is used. Where a motorway terminates at a grade separated junction, the advance direction signs will be designed in the same way as for intermediate junctions. Panels are not used, and route numbers are in the Motorway alphabet. The map type roundabout signs shown in diagrams 2913.1 and 2914.1 are used where the roundabout connects two motorways. Motorway numbers on these signs are shown in the Motorway alphabet and coloured panels are used only if the signs indicate, additionally, a route that is not a motorway.

10.16 On map type advance direction signs on the main carriageway, the forward destinations do not normally include the motorway numbers. However, where the number of another motorway that can be reached from a junction ahead is shown in brackets, the characters should be from the Transport Medium alphabet and not the Motorway alphabet.

10.17 On gantry mounted signs, bracketed route numbers may be in either the Motorway or Transport Medium alphabet as appropriate. The general rule is that where the number is directly associated with an unbracketed number the Motorway alphabet should be used, as illustrated in diagram 2908. Where the bracketed route number follows a place name or is a destination in its own right, the Transport Medium alphabet should be used.

10.18 A combined junction number and distance plate (in Transport Medium alphabet) may be provided on sign gantries. The design of this plate is shown in figure 10-9.

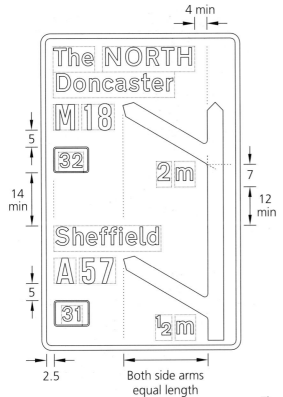

Figure 10-8

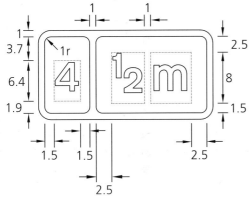

Figure 10-9

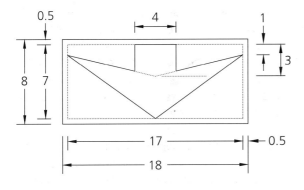

Figure 10-10

10.19 Where gantry signs indicate a lane drop (diagrams 2908.1 and 2909), the downward pointing arrow is shown on a blue patch placed directly on the gantry structure (i.e. separate from the main sign). The design of this patch is shown in figure 10-10. The slip road gantry sign shown in diagram 2913.4 follows the design rules set out in section 9.

10.20 Symbols, other than the aircraft, ferry and railway station symbols, are not permitted on blue background motorway signs. However, they may be incorporated in all-purpose road destination panels on signs such as those located on exit slip roads and on the approach to a terminal roundabout.

10.21 Similarly, warning and regulatory signs may be incorporated only on motorway signs that include all-purpose road destination panels.

10.22 The design of rectangular direction signs located on the nose of an exit slip road is shown on working drawing P 2910 & P 2910.1.

ROUTE CONFIRMATORY SIGNS ON MOTORWAYS

10.23 The design of route confirmatory signs is similar to those on all-purpose roads as described in paras 8.1 to 8.8. Figure 10-11 shows the appropriate design rules to accommodate the Motorway alphabet used for the route numbers. As for other motorway signs, where the motorway number at the top of the sign is bracketed, the gap to the top border is increased to 4 sw. Distances must be to the nearest mile, as fractions are not permitted on motorway signs.

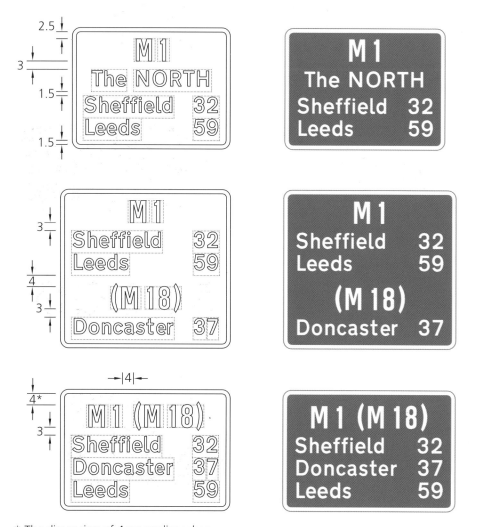

* The dimension of 4 sw applies when the motorway number is bracketed

Figure 10-11

CANCELLED ROUTE NUMBERS

11.1 Item 20 of Schedule 16 to the Regulations permits superseded route numbers with red cancellation bars to be shown on directional signs. Figure 11-1 shows the design of the bar and figure 11-2 shows the appropriate vertical and horizontal spaces to adjacent legends and symbols. Unlike the "no through road" symbol (see figure 5-45), the red bar does not have a white border when placed on a dark background.

11.2 In the case of the "Cambridge - Newmarket" example in figure 11-2, the vertical block spacing to "Ely" is increased from 2 sw to 4 sw. This is because "Newmarket" is placed above its associated route numbers and the red bar necessitates a line spacing of 1.5 sw as shown. The increased block spacing ensures that the A14 route number is associated with "Cambridge" and "Newmarket". Where route numbers are on the same line as their associated destinations, the standard block spacing of 2 sw is appropriate as shown in the "Corby - Leicester" example.

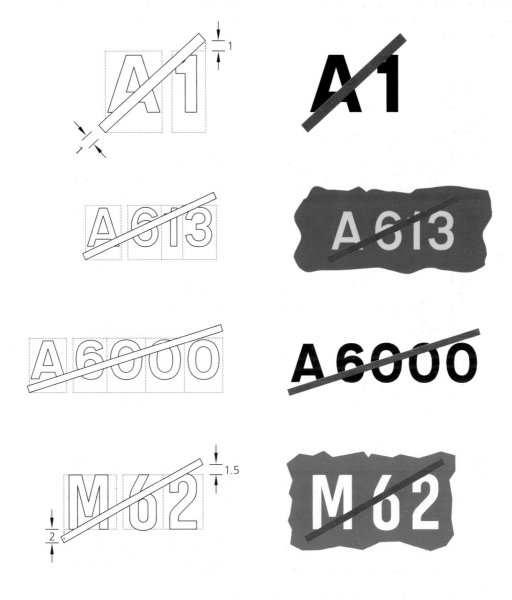

Figure 11-1

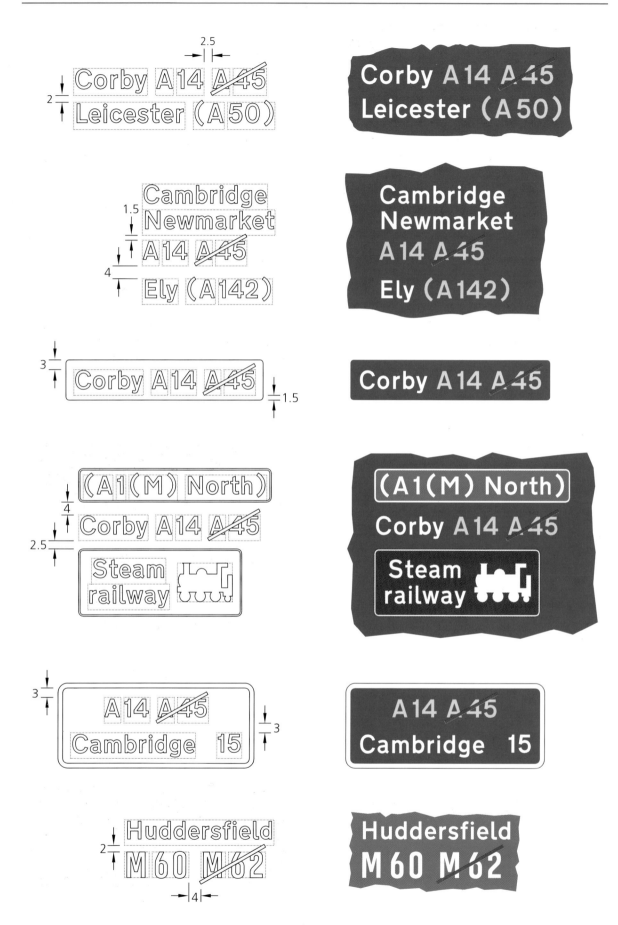

Figure 11-2

A 14 previously A 45

Figure 11-3

11.3 As an alternative to the cancellation bar, a separate temporary black on yellow sign may be provided indicating the change in route number. This can be mounted either on its own or beneath a permanent advance direction sign. An example is illustrated in figure 11-3. This sign must not be retained for more than two years (see para 14.2).

DIVERSION ROUTE SYMBOLS

11.4 Schedule 13 Part VII of the Regulations shows the symbols that may be added to permanent directional informatory signs to indicate a route to be followed when a motorway or high standard

all-purpose road is closed during an emergency or during major maintenance or construction works. The design of these symbols is shown on working drawing S 56. Figures 11-4 and 11-5 show how the symbols are added to the destination blocks on the permanent signs. It should be noted that the symbol is always on a yellow patch whatever the background colour of the main sign. The symbol should always be associated with the route number of the road to be followed until the road or motorway to which the road user is returning is shown on the signs. The symbol should then be associated with this route number. The symbol may be shown on a destination panel, but never on a green or blue route number patch. The symbol should be placed to the right of or below the appropriate route number.

11.5 Where separate signs to diagrams 2703 and 2704 are used to indicate symbolic diversion routes, reference should be made to the working drawings for design details.

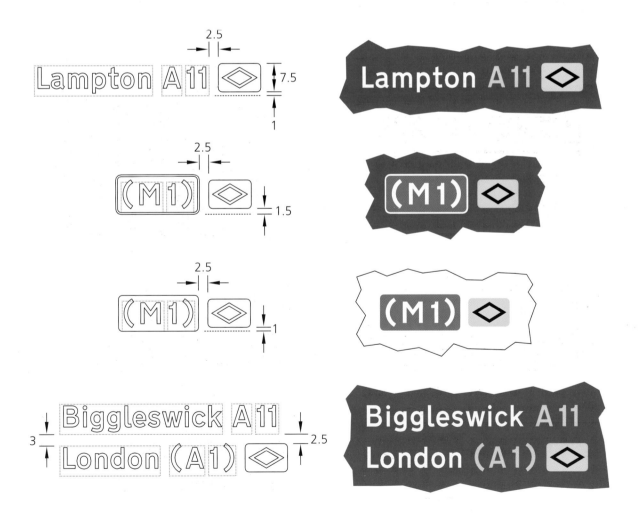

Figure 11-4

3.5   2.5

3   2.5

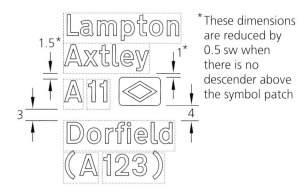

* These dimensions are reduced by 0.5 sw when there is no descender above the symbol patch

1.5*   1*

3   4

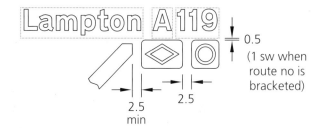 

0.5
(1 sw when route no is bracketed)

2.5
min

2.5

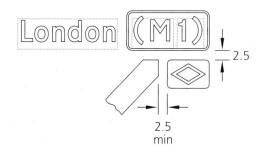 

2.5

2.5
min

Figure 11-5

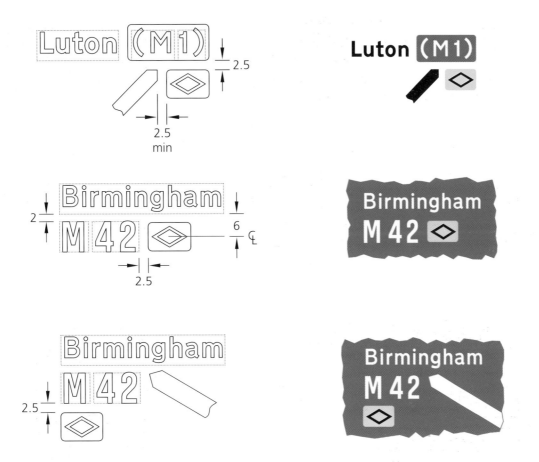

Figure 11-5 (continued)

ALTERATIONS TO EXISTING SIGNS

11.6 Existing signs sometimes need to be altered to take account of the opening to traffic of a new road, or other changes to the highway network such as reclassification. These alterations can take the form of new or deleted destinations, changes to route numbers etc. To save the cost of providing a completely new replacement sign, it is often possible to modify an existing sign by the application of cover plates. *In no circumstances may smaller x-heights or sub-standard spacings be used to accommodate alterations*.

11.7 Care should be taken to ensure that the sign face materials used to manufacture a cover plate match as far as is possible the materials used for the manufacture of the original sign. Problems that are likely to occur are mis-matched colours and mis-matched retroreflective properties. It is not uncommon to recognise a plated sign at night by a highly reflective "panel" on what is otherwise a relatively dark sign. Such methods of sign

modification should be avoided, as they give unwarranted emphasis to a particular section of the sign. Where the intention is to remove the plates at a future date, they should be affixed to the sign in a manner that does not cause damage to the original sign face (other than the drilling of holes).

11.8 Where future changes are anticipated, it may be possible to design a sign with these changes in mind. However, the initial design of the sign should follow the design rules detailed in this chapter.

11.9 Where a sign is altered by the application of plates, and the sign had not previously been designed to take account of the specific changes, care must be taken to ensure that the modified sign still accords with the design rules, particularly with respect to block spacing. On map type signs it is important that the minimum space for unrelated blocks is maintained. Where a place name is removed from a list of destinations, a single line cover plate should not be used if this produces an artificial gap in the list. In this case a complete cover plate containing

Existing sign

Incorrect plating

Correct plating

New sign

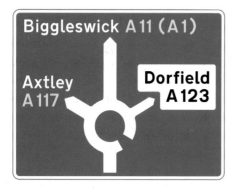

Existing sign

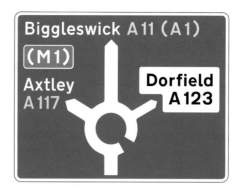

Incorrect plating

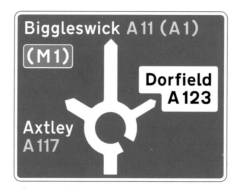

Correct plating

Figure 11-6

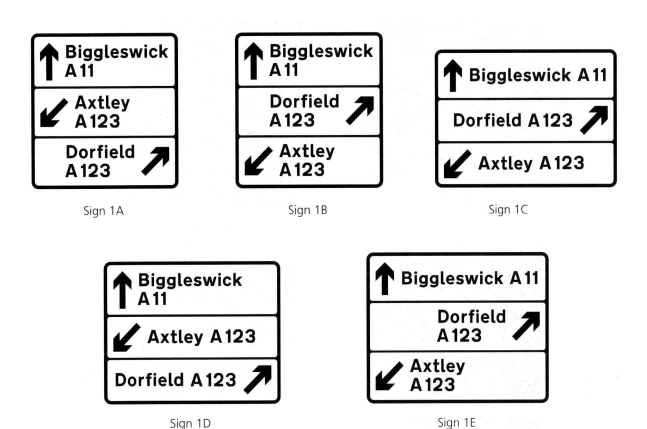

Sign 1A Sign 1B Sign 1C

Sign 1D Sign 1E

Figure 11-7

the retained place names should be provided for the entire destination block. Where additional place names are added, it may be necessary to use abbreviations (see para 2.11). Examples of the correct and incorrect use of cover plates are shown in figure 11-6, which also illustrates, for comparison purposes, the alternative solution of providing a complete new sign.

11.10 Where a satisfactory sign cannot be produced by modifying the existing sign, and where the provision of a new replacement sign is ruled out on the grounds of cost, consideration should be given to the provision of a separately mounted supplementary sign showing the new information. Minor modifications may still need to be made to the existing sign. A new sign, replacing both the existing and supplementary signs, can be provided at a future date when funds permit or as part of a maintenance programme. Where there is likely to be a series of changes to a particular sign brought about by the progressive opening of a new road, consideration should be given to the provision of supplementary signs and minor modifications to the existing sign, with a view to providing a new sign once all the changes have taken place.

GENERAL DESIGN CONSIDERATIONS

11.11 By following the design rules for directional informatory signs covered in sections 3 to 11, it is possible to produce different layouts for the same sign. Figures 11-7 to 11-13 show some examples, described below in more detail.

11.12 Figure 11-7 is a stack type sign showing a simple crossroads where the side roads enter at an angle. Only one destination and route number is shown for each direction. Sign 1A is the smallest of the group, but is a little cluttered as there are two lines for each directional panel. The panels are stacked in the conventional order, that is left turn above right turn. Sign 1B differs only in that the right turn is shown above the left turn. This sign is easier to understand, as the pattern of the arrows emphasizes the junction layout. Sign 1C improves the clarity of the sign further by placing the route numbers alongside the place names. The arrows now determine the height of each directional panel, creating additional space between the legends and the panel dividers/sign borders. This extra space makes the sign easier to read. This sign, being wider than sign 1B, may be more suited to footway

Sign 2A

Sign 2B

Sign 2C

Sign 2D

Figure 11-8

mounting where sufficient width is required between the posts to allow the passage of pedestrians with wheelchairs or prams. As the ahead destination determines the width of the sign, by placing this on two lines (sign 1D), the sign width can be reduced slightly where verge or footway width is limited. This modification of the design is at the expense of a taller and larger sign. Finally, sign 1E demonstrates a poor design. This is the largest sign in the group and the arrangement of route numbers does nothing to improve the appearance of the sign.

11.13 Figure 11-8 is a map type sign showing the same junction as figure 11-7, except that the A11 has primary route status in this example. The sign therefore demonstrates the use of coloured panels. Sign 2A shows the conventional layout. The "Dorfield" panel has the route number ranged right to allow the route arm to tuck into the destination block. The vertical separation of the two side destinations ("Axtley" and "Dorfield") helps to emphasize the junction layout. Sign 2B has about the

same area as sign 2A. The panel positions in sign 2B emphasize the crossroads even further. There is no doubt that "Axtley" is to the left and "Dorfield" to the right. With this arrangement it is not possible to tuck the right turn route arm into the "Dorfield" panel and therefore the route number is ranged left. If the height of the sign were increased, the right turn in sign 2B could be designed as for sign 2A. This would reduce the width of the sign, but the left and right destination panels would be out of balance ("Dorfield" being closer to the vertical route arm than "Axtley"). Sign 2C reduces the sign area to a minimum. However, the short approach arm and the position of the side destination panels do not adequately illustrate the junction layout. Although a space saver, this sign design is not recommended. Sign 2D is similar to sign 2A except that the right turn destination panel is positioned below the route arm. Because the route arm is angled upwards, it tends to dissociate itself from the destination panel. However, the design does work, and because the right turn panel is higher than the left turn panel the nature of

Sign 3A
Area 5% larger than Sign 3B

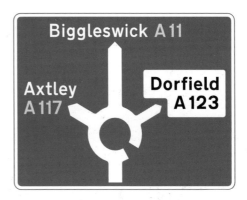

Sign 3B

Figure 11-9

the crossroads is still clear. Had the left turn been at 90°, the "Axtley" panel in sign 2D would have been higher on the sign and the junction layout would be much clearer with the "Dorfield" panel positioned as in sign 2A. Destination blocks should not generally be placed beneath a route arm that angles upwards by more than 30° to the horizontal.

11.14 Figure 11-9 shows a roundabout with two upward pointing side arms. Sign 3A shows the conventional design. Sign 3B allows the right turn arm to tuck into the destination block, resulting in a slight reduction of the overall sign area. It should be noted that the sign height has been increased to maintain the correct vertical block spacing between the forward destination and the "Dorfield" panel.

Sign 4A

Sign 4B

Sign 4C

Sign 4D
Area 7% larger than Sign 4C

Figure 11-10

11.15 Figure 11-10 shows a final advance direction sign on a motorway. Sign 4A is the conventional design with the junction number in the bottom left hand corner. By moving the junction number to the top left hand corner, as shown on sign 4B, and lowering the side destination block, the height of the sign (and hence overall area) can be substantially reduced. However, this was only possible because the horizontal length of the forward destination was very short. Signs 4C and 4D demonstrate that with a longer length of forward destination, the smaller sign is the one with the junction number at the bottom. Another consideration is the length of the bottom line of the side destination. Although this can be positioned close to the bottom border, as shown on sign 4B, this may not be possible when the distance to the junction is added. Also, as one mile and 1/2 mile advance direction signs do not normally show a forward destination, there would be no saving on the height of the sign by placing the junction number at the top.

11.16 The design rules in previous sections show how triangular warning signs and regulatory roundel signs are added to direction and advance direction signs. The more complex the information given within the triangle or roundel, the larger it needs to be, relative to the main sign, to ensure that it is still legible to drivers (see Appendix D for sizes). Where this results in very large signs with significant amounts of blank space, consideration should be given to placing the warning/regulatory information on separate signs, and not integrating it into the main direction and advance direction signs. Where an advance direction sign incorporates both an imperial and a metric warning sign, care must be taken to minimise wasted space. Figure 11-11 shows a sign for a three-way junction where the ahead route has a height restriction. The design of sign 5A assumes that the imperial triangle (which must always appear to the *left* of the pair) should be placed on the vertical route arm. However, this results in an overlarge sign. By placing the metric warning sign on the vertical arm, as shown in sign 5B, a more efficient design is achieved. Depending on the number of destinations shown, and the length of the place name blocks, it may be possible to reduce the area of the sign face further by using a stack type sign as shown in sign 5C.

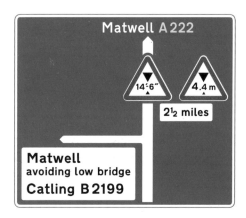

Sign 5A

Sign 5B

Sign 5C

Figure 11-11

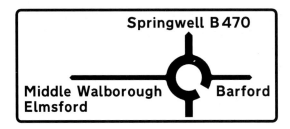

AREA = 100%
(100% without Elmsford)

Sign 6A

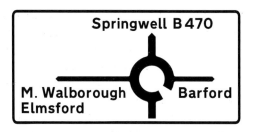

AREA = 88%
(88% without Elmsford)

Sign 6B

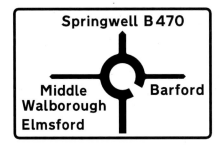

AREA = 88%
(76% without Elmsford)

Sign 6C

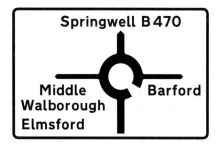

Sign 6D

Figure 11-12

11.17 Place names with two or more words lend themselves to alternative layouts. Figure 11-12 shows an example of a map type roundabout sign with the destination "Middle Walborough" indicated along an unnumbered non-primary route. On sign 6A "Middle Walborough" is on a single line; this results in a very large sign which is wasteful of space. In the example, the destination to the right has a relatively short name (Barford) and, with the extremely long left turn arm, the complete map type route symbol looks out of balance. The total area of the sign can be reduced by 12% by abbreviating "Middle Walborough" to "M. Walborough" as shown on sign 6B. One problem here is that should there be another destination with a similar name, such as "Market Walborough", not too far away and not indicated on the sign, confusion could arise. It is generally better to avoid using abbreviations, and to place the name on two lines as shown on sign 6C. The width of the sign is reduced further, although the height is increased, resulting in a sign that has the same area as sign 6B. However, in addition to showing the place name in full, sign 6C has a more balanced route symbol layout, and the reduced width will help to overcome any siting difficulties. As this is a roundabout junction, "Walborough", being on the second line, tucks under the route symbol. This is a contributory factor to the reduction in sign width. If "Middle Walborough" was the only destination to be signed to the left, the omission of "Elmsford" would not affect the size of signs 6A and 6B, as the height is determined by the minimum length of the approach arm (see para 5.39). However, the height of sign 6C would be the same as 6A and 6B, resulting in a total sign area equal to 76% of that for sign 6A. The difference between signs 6C and 6D is in the length of the left turn route arm. On sign 6C the two-thirds rule (see para 5.6) is applied to the longest part of the block (i.e. "Walborough"). This results in the arm almost passing the first part of the name ("Middle"). The passing effect would be further exaggerated had the place name been "Old Walborough" on two lines. On sign 6D, the appearance of the route arm is improved by applying the two-thirds rule to "Middle" rather than to "Walborough". There may be other situations where applying the two-thirds rule to the line of legend immediately below the route arm improves the appearance of the sign.

11.18 An error commonly seen on both panelled advance direction signs and flag type direction signs is the inefficient layout of multi-part names. Figure 11-13 shows a flag type direction sign indicating a business park, with a three word name. The most economical design for this particular example is to place the destination on two lines, but the difference in area between signs 7A and 7B shows that substantial savings can be made by choosing the appropriate pairing of words. Sign 7A is likely to be used only where it is to be mounted on a backing board with another flag sign of a similar length. Using flag signs of similar length produces a more balanced assembly of signs. Placing the destination on three lines, as shown on sign 7C, increases the height of the sign with only a marginal saving in the overall length. Although the legend block is shorter than that on sign 7B, the chevron takes up more horizontal space because it has increased height and width. The gap between the chevron and the border of the pointing end of the sign is also increased. (See figure 7-1 for chevron sizes.) The most efficient layout in any particular case will of course depend upon the relative lengths of the words involved.

WORKING DRAWINGS FOR DIRECTIONAL INFORMATORY SIGNS

11.19 Working drawings in the "P" series, included in the list at Appendix A, are available for certain diagrams in Schedule 7 to the Regulations. These drawings cover special features not dealt with in this chapter. Sets of working drawings can be obtained from the Stationery Office or from the Department's website.

AREA = 100%

Sign 7A

AREA = 75%

Sign 7B

Stocksford Business Park

AREA = 87%

Sign 7C

Figure 11-13

INTRODUCTION

12.1 The design of regulatory roundel signs is covered by the "P" series of working drawings. This section deals with those signs that are designed to be used with specific traffic regulation orders. The most common type of sign is the waiting and/or loading restriction time plate.

12.2 The following rules cover some of the designs permitted by the Regulations. The signs to which these rules are applicable are listed in the table at Appendix E. It is intended that more detailed designs will be included in a revised Chapter 3.

12.3 The design rules in this section supplement those given in section 2. Particular attention is drawn to para 2.10 and figure 2-2 which deal with horizontal spacing of abbreviated words.

12.4 The alphabet used is the Transport Heavy alphabet, all characters being black. Signs, or parts of signs, indicating waiting restrictions and the prohibition of stopping have yellow backgrounds. Those signs, or parts of signs, indicating no loading or types of parking, such as pay and display, have white backgrounds.

TIME OF DAY

12.5 Times are expressed in hours and minutes and as either "am" or "pm". The 24 hour clock is not used. Where the sign indicates a 24 hour restriction or prohibition, the time period is either omitted or expressed as "At any time" (or "at any time" as shown in diagram 638). Schedule 16, item 38 of the Regulations lists those signs that may use the expression "At any time" or "at any time".

12.6 A time period is shown as a start and end time separated by a hyphen. Where both the start and end times are whole hours, minutes are not shown (e.g. 8 am). However, where the start time for a particular period is not immediately followed by "am" or "pm" and either the start or end time shows minutes (e.g. 7.30) then the other time should also show minutes even though this may be zero (e.g. 9.00). Examples of time periods are "7.30 - 9.00 am", "7 - 9 am", "7 am - 6 pm" and "7 am - 6.30 pm". Examples of combinatións that are not recommended are "7 - 9.30 am" and "7.30 - 9 am". Where two time periods are shown on the same sign, one period may

be expressed in hours only and the other in hours and minutes as appropriate.

12.7 If the time period covers only "am" or "pm", but not both, then "am" or "pm", as appropriate, should be shown only against the end time.

12.8 12 noon and 12 midnight should be expressed as "Noon" (or "Midday") and "Midnight" (or "M'night") respectively. Where a time period spans midnight, it should be expressed as two separate time periods, the first commencing at midnight and the second ending at midnight, unless the same time period applies on every day of the week.

12.9 Figure 12-1 shows the various combinations of time periods and the appropriate horizontal spacing. Where more than one time period is shown, the tiles of each are butted vertically. On some signs a single time period may be shown on two lines.

Varies according to
overall width of sign

Figure 12-1

DAY OF THE WEEK

12.10 Should the restriction or prohibition apply for a single day, or a specified time period applies for one particular day, the name of the day should appear in full (e.g. Saturday). Where a period is expressed as a number of consecutive days, the start and end days should be abbreviated and separated by a hyphen. Should the period be only two consecutive days, the hyphen may be replaced by an ampersand (&). A list of abbreviations and the appropriate horizontal spacing is shown in figure 12-2.

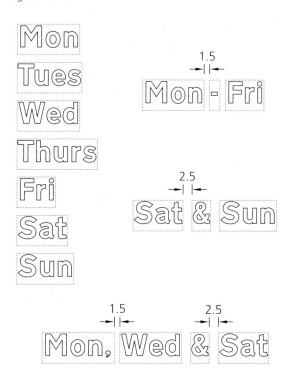

Figure 12-2

TIME OF YEAR

12.11 Where the restriction or prohibition applies for only part of the year, the appropriate dates are added to the sign. These can be expressed as specific dates, or months only, to accord with the traffic regulation order. Expressions such as "Term time" (to reflect school periods) are not permitted, but where a named day such as "Good Friday" is consistent throughout the country and familiar to road users, this may be used. References to bank or public holidays are permitted by the Regulations.

12.12 Figure 12-3 gives a list of abbreviations and shows the appropriate horizontal spaces when setting out a date and a date period.

Figure 12-3

COMBINING TIMES, DAYS AND DATES

12.13 The sequence of setting out the above information on the sign is, from top to bottom: "days", "times" and "dates". Each line is centred horizontally and the vertical gap between each element is shown in figure 12-4. Figure 12-4 also shows how to combine more than one time period.

Figure 12-4

SUPPLEMENTARY LEGENDS

12.14 Some time plates may have supplementary legends such as "except taxis" and "on school entrance markings". These legends are generally placed below the day/time/date legend and separated vertically from the line above by 1 sw. An example is given in figure 12-5.

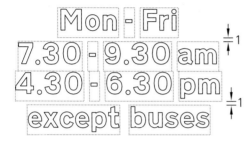

Figure 12-5

MODEL LAYOUTS FOR WAITING, STOPPING AND LOADING PROHIBITION TIME PLATES

12.15 Figure 12-6 sets out basic models for waiting, stopping or loading prohibition time plates. The roundel for the waiting prohibition is taken from working drawing P 636 and reduced to the appropriate size. A diameter of 8 sw is generally used where the time plate is used in conjunction with yellow road markings. Time plates that are not used with road markings (e.g. diagram 637.2) use a larger roundel size of 20 sw diameter. For the design of signs with the larger roundel, reference should be made to the working drawings, but the basic rules above for setting out time periods still apply (see also para 12.16). The roundel for the prohibition of stopping is taken from working drawing P 642 and reduced to the appropriate size. This roundel is always accompanied by the legend "No stopping".

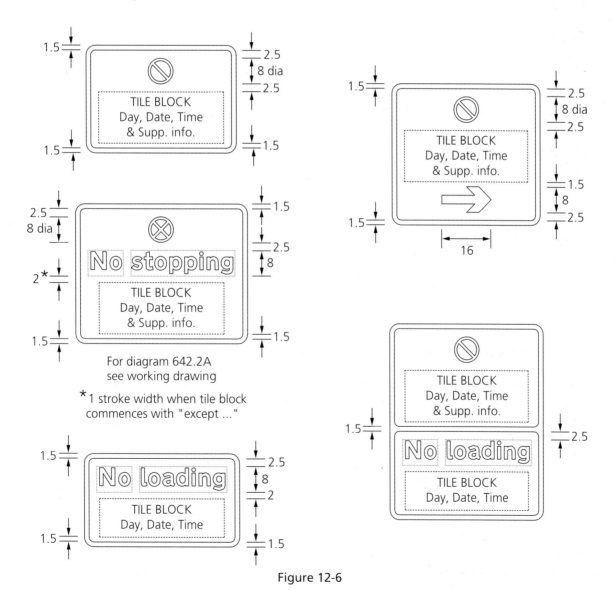

Figure 12-6

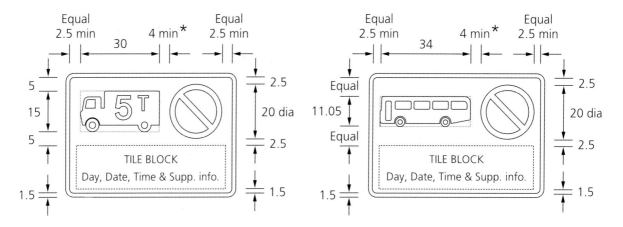

*This dimension is equal to the gap between symbols and the side borders when these are greater than 4 stroke widths

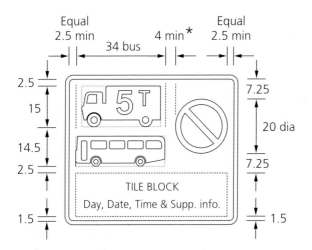

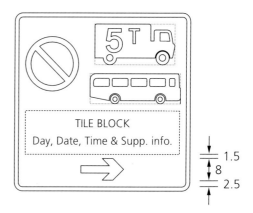

Symbols are reversed as shown when a right-pointing arrow is added to the sign

Figure 12-7

12.16 Waiting prohibitions sometimes apply only to goods or commercial vehicles. Where the prohibition applies only to goods vehicles, the lorry symbol shown on working drawing S 32 is placed alongside the "no waiting" roundel. A lorry together with a bus symbol (working drawing S 25) denotes that the prohibition applies to commercial vehicles. Where the prohibition applies to public service vehicles only, the bus symbol alone is used with the "no waiting" roundel. Typical examples are shown in figure 12-7.

12.17 In some cases, it may be possible to reduce the sign height by placing the "no waiting" roundel to the side of the time period (see diagrams 639.1B and 640). Design details are shown in figure 12-8.

MODEL LAYOUTS FOR LIMITED WAITING TIME PLATES

12.18 Limited waiting time plates use the "P" parking symbol shown on working drawing S 43. The size is 20 sw square. Figure 12-9 sets out the basic model for the sign design which may be combined with waiting prohibition plates as shown in diagram 639.1B. The maximum duration that parking is permitted, or the period during which a return is prohibited may be shown as hours or minutes: "minutes" may be abbreviated to "mins"; "hours" will generally be shown in full. Reference should be made to the working drawings for the shared parking bay signs shown in diagrams 660.6 and 660.7.

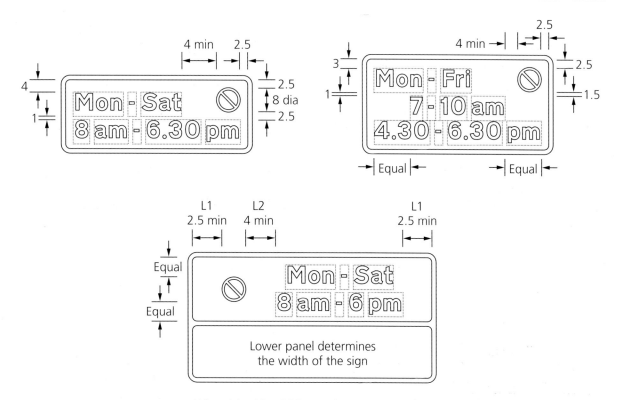

When L1 + L2 + L1 is equal to or greater than
12 stroke widths, L1 should always equal L2

Figure 12-8

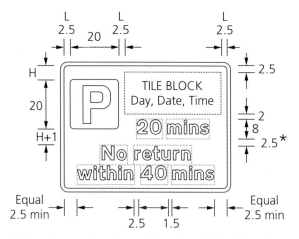

When bottom line determines the width of the sign
the value of L is increased from 2.5 stroke widths
maintaining equal spacing at the top of the sign

*This dimension is reduced to 2 stroke widths
when the upper block (20 mins in the example)
is centred horizontally over the "No return" block
(see working drawing for diagram 660.6)

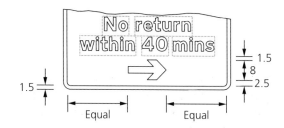

Figure 12-9

ZONE ENTRY SIGNS

12.19 Zone entry signs will usually include a time
plate. The manner in which these are added to the
signs, and the appropriate colours, are shown in the
diagrams in Schedule 2 to the Regulations. The plate
design follows the same rules as described above.

OTHER DESIGN DETAILS

12.20 Appendix E includes in note 3 a list of those
diagrams for which reference to the "P" series of
working drawings should be made.

13 SIGNS FOR ROAD WORKS

INTRODUCTION

13.1 This section covers the design of signs for lane restrictions and lane changes on motorways and all-purpose dual carriageway roads as described in Chapter 8. These signs are shown in diagrams 7201, 7201.1, 7210 to 7240 inclusive and 7260 to 7288 inclusive in Schedule 12 to the Regulations. Other signs in Schedule 12 are detailed in the "P" series of working drawings (see Appendix A).

13.2 The complete signs, shown in diagrams 7201, 7201.1 and 7210 to 7240 inclusive, are illustrated in Appendix F. These generally comprise three sign panels, the central panel forming the main sign. The top panels, shown in diagrams 7260 to 7264 inclusive, and the bottom panels, shown in diagrams 7270 to 7275 inclusive, are also illustrated in Appendix F. The combinations of top and bottom panels which may be used with each main sign are shown in the table of combinations accompanying each diagram. Reference should therefore be made to the Regulations when designing any of these signs. Diagram 7201.1 does not have a table of combinations.

13.3 The main element of the signs shown in diagrams 7201, 7201.1 and 7210 to 7240 (generally the central panel) can be varied to suit the circumstances. Diagrams 7280 to 7288 inclusive show these variations. Additionally, the number of arrows and the position of the red blocks representing the closed areas of carriageway may be varied. Signs to diagrams 7201 and 7201.1 do not use red blocks.

13.4 The sign elements shown in diagrams 7280 to 7286 inclusive may be used with all the main signs. Diagram 7287 (red bar denoting a closed lane ahead) may be used only with diagram 7201, and diagram 7288 (white downward pointing arrow) which indicates a contra-flow system is in operation, may be used only with diagram 7201.1. It should be noted that this arrow in diagram 7288 represents the opposing flow of traffic, and therefore only one arrow should be used, irrespective of the number of opposing lanes. Because the contrast between white and yellow is poor, especially when daylight is fading, it is important to ensure that the black border, which provides the outline to the white arrow, has the correct width (see figure 13-3).

13.5 The regulatory signs shown in diagrams 7282 to 7284.1 inclusive show measurements for weight, width and height restrictions (see figure 13-3). There are two sizes; 750 mm diameter for imperial-only signs and 900 mm for metric/imperial width and height restriction signs (diagrams 7283.1 and 7284.1). The 900 mm weight limit sign (diagram 7282) is used only when placed on a sign which incorporates either diagram 7283.1 or 7284.1. All roundels on a particular sign should have the same diameter (e.g. diagrams 7283 and 7284.1 should not be used on the same sign - both restrictions should be either imperial only or metric/imperial). *Metric-only roundel signs must not be used*.

13.6 There is only one prescribed size for each of the various components that make up the complete sign. Therefore, the dimensions are given in millimetres rather than stroke widths. This is particularly useful as the complete signs will generally have different x-heights for particular legends (e.g. the top panel has an x-height of 150 mm and the bottom panel has an x-height of 165 mm). A stroke width dimension could not, therefore, be easily related to an x-height. For those using computer aided design, where stroke width dimensions would be easier to handle than millimetres, it is suggested that a stroke width of 25 mm is assumed (nominal x-height 100 mm). All dimensions in the following figures can then be converted to stroke widths by multiplying by a factor of 0.04. Care will need to be taken when applying these stroke width dimensions as the various x-heights will not be equivalent to 4 sw. Other elements will also have non-standard sizes (e.g. border width is 2 sw and arrow head width is 9.6 sw).

DESIGN OF TOP AND BOTTOM PANELS

13.7 The legend in the top panel is *always in black capital letters* (Transport Heavy alphabet) on a *yellow background.* Design details are shown in figure 13-1.

13.8 The number of lines of legend in the top panel will depend on the overall width of the sign. Where the top panel is the critical element in determining the width of the sign, the legend should be on two lines if this results in a reduction in the overall size of the sign, or where the width of the sign needs to be kept to a minimum for siting purposes.

13.9 The legend in the bottom panel is *always in black lower case letters* (Transport Heavy alphabet) other than the first character of a worded legend which will be in upper case. The background colour

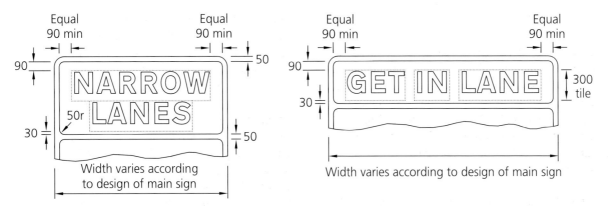

All dimensions are in millimetres - x-height is 150 mm

Figure 13-1

is *always yellow.* Design details are shown in figure 13-2.

13.10 Where the number of lines in the bottom panel can be varied, the appropriate layout will be

the one that optimises the overall size of the sign, or produces the minimum width where siting constraints are a consideration. Where the distance in diagram 7271 is on two lines, the legend "yards" should not be abbreviated to "yds".

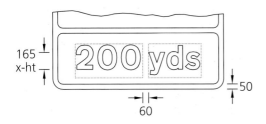

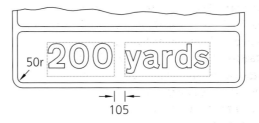

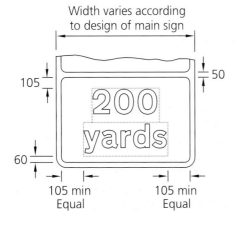

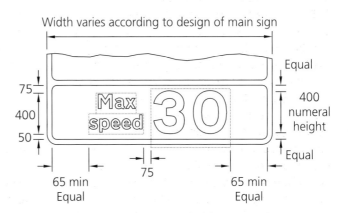

All dimensions are in millimetres

Figure 13-2

DESIGN ELEMENTS FOR THE CENTRE PANEL

13.11 Diagrams 7280 to 7288 inclusive show the various options that are available. The design of each of these elements is shown in figure 13-3. It should be noted that diagram 7285 is used only on signs to be placed on all-purpose roads and that diagram 7286 should be used only on signs that are placed on motorways. The alphabet used for the route number in diagram 7286 is the Motorway Black alphabet

shown in Schedule 13 Part IV to the Regulations. Because the characters occupy the full tile height, the x-height is smaller than that of diagram 7285 in order to produce a more balanced overall sign layout. The top of the red bar in diagram 7287 should be positioned 300 mm below the top of any adjacent arrow which forms part of any other sign element (see figure 13-7). This is to ensure a clear distinction between open and closed lanes when the sign is viewed from a distance.

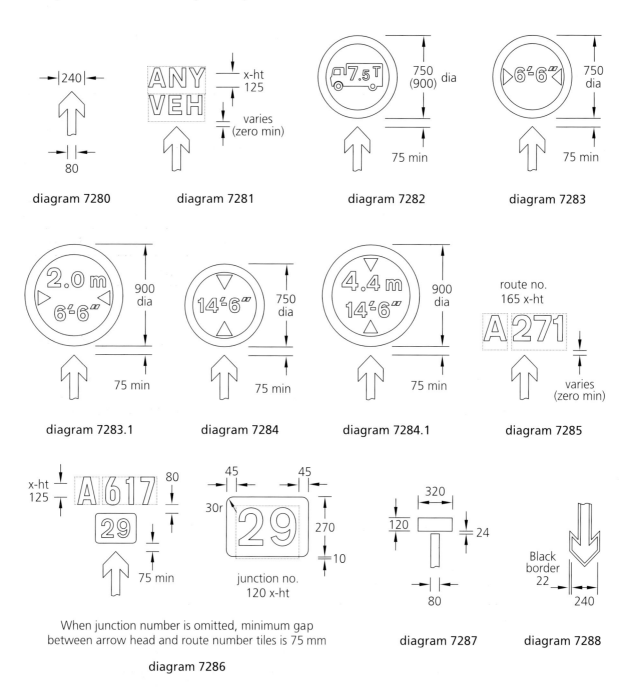

All dimensions are in millimetres

Figure 13-3

13.12 The horizontal space between arrow centres depends on which two diagrams from 7280 to 7288 inclusive are next to each other. The table in figure 13-4 shows the appropriate spacings for each combination, together with the distance to a side border or lane line. These are minimum values, and should be increased (a) where the width of the sign is determined by either the top or bottom panel, or (b) where an increase in the horizontal spaces improves the sign layout. Figure 13-5 details the minimum gap between various elements and the top border, panel divider or horizontal bar.

HORIZONTAL SPACES BETWEEN THE VARIOUS ELEMENTS OF THE CENTRE PANEL (millimetres)

Diagram	7280	7281	7282 7283 7284 (750mm)	7282 7283.1 7284.1 (900mm)	7285 7286	7287	7288	Border
7280	400	600	700	775	325	400	400	225
7281	600	750	750	825	475	550	600	375
7282/3/4 (750mm)	700	750	870	—	475	650	700	475
7282/3.1/4.1 (900mm)	775	825	—	1020	550	725	775	550
7285/6	325	475	475	550	200	275	325	100
7287	400	550	650	725	275	400	—	260
7288	400	600	700	775	325	—	—	250
Border	225	375	475	550	100	260	250	—

NOTES

1. The above dimensions are *minimum* values. They may be increased to improve the appearance of the sign or where either the top or bottom panel determines the width of the sign.

2. Measurements are taken from the centre line of each arrow, the inside edge of any sign border, or the edge of any lane line, central reservation symbol or red block representing the closed area of carriageway. *In the case of diagrams 7285 and 7286 the measurement is made from the edge of the tile block.* In the case of diagram 7287 the measurement is taken from the centre line of the shaft.

Figure 13-4

VERTICAL SPACES BETWEEN THE VARIOUS ELEMENTS OF THE CENTRE PANEL AND
THE UPPER BORDER, PANEL DIVIDER OR HORIZONTAL BAR (minimum values)

Arrow head (diagram 7280)	150 mm
Roundel (diagrams 7282, 7283 , 7283.1, 7284 and 7284.1)	100 mm
Legend tiles (diagrams 7281, 7285 and 7286)	100 mm
Contra-flow arrow (diagram 7288)	150 mm

Figure 13-5

DESIGN OF DIAGRAMS 7201 AND 7201.1

13.13 Diagram 7201 is used on the approach to road works and diagram 7201.1 as a repeater sign through the works. These signs do not indicate any lane changes or show red blocks denoting areas of closed carriageway. Diagram 7201.1 may incorporate diagram 7288 (white downward pointing arrow) to indicate contra-flow operation (see para 13.4). Figure 13-6 shows a design example for each diagram.

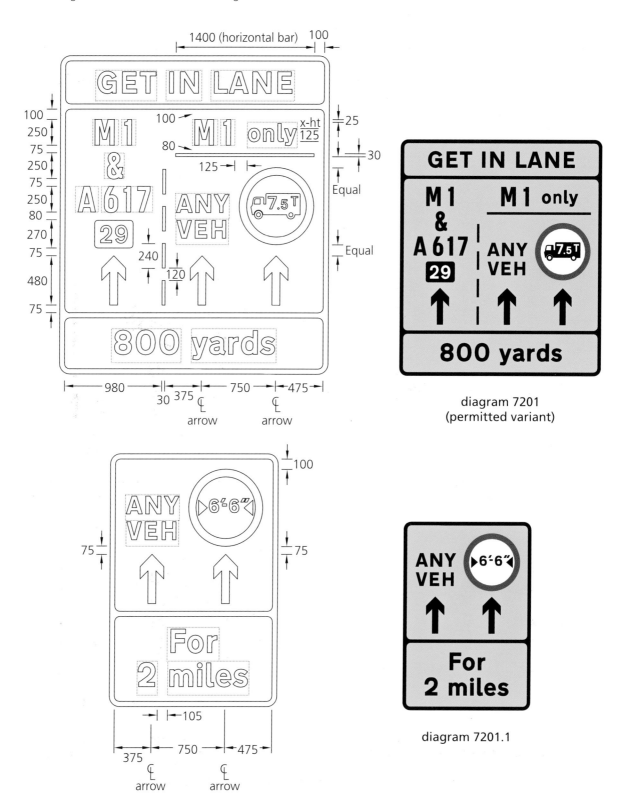

diagram 7201
(permitted variant)

diagram 7201.1

Figure 13-6

13.14 Although vertical lane lines are optional, they should always be used to differentiate between different destinations in diagram 7201. The length of the line is variable and may extend to the top of the panel should this give a clearer indication of the appropriate lanes to be used by traffic. The lane line shown in figure 13-6 does not extend to the top of the panel, as M1 traffic can use all lanes. Where two or more lanes lead to the same destination which is shown only once, a horizontal bar should be used as shown. Where two adjacent arrows are both to diagram 7285 or 7286 and show the same route number, a horizontal bar is not used (see diagram 7233 as an example).

13.15 The horizontal spacing of elements in the centre panel is shown in the table in figure 13-4. It should be noted that the sign should contain at least one of the elements shown in diagrams 7281 to 7286 inclusive. Where the sign would be made up

only from a combination of diagrams 7280 and 7287 or 7288, a "wicket" type sign from the 7202 to 7209 series should be used instead of diagrams 7201 or 7201.1. The only exception to this rule is where diagram 7264 (NARROW LANES) is required as a top panel on diagram 7201.

13.16 Where the overall width of the sign is determined by either the top or bottom panel, the horizontal spaces between the individual arrows should be increased. Where arrows are equally spaced, the increased space should be split equally between each arrow. Where the arrows are not equally spaced (see table in figure 13-4) the additional space should be apportioned so that the arrows approach equal spacing. Should equal spacing be achieved before using up all the additional width, the remaining space would be split equally between each arrow. An example is shown in figure 13-7.

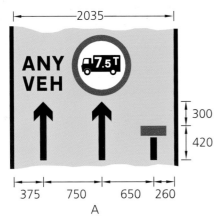

A: Minimum widths in accordance with the table in figure 13-4.

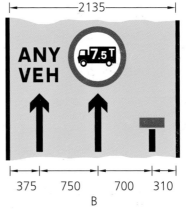

B: Width of sign increased. Additional width apportioned to the two smaller right hand widths.

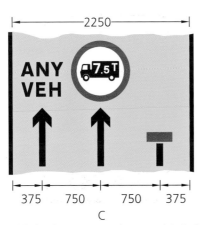

C: Width further increased to provide balanced spacing based on the two left hand widths.

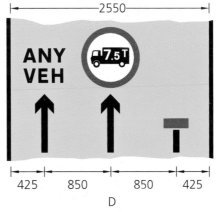

D: Width further increased with the centre lines of the shafts positioned at the quarter points.

Width of signs B, C and D determined by either the top or bottom panel.

Figure 13-7

13.17 The length of the vertical arrow is generally 480 mm (see figure 13-6). However, when the sign incorporates diagram 7287 (lane closed), the arrow length is increased to 720 mm; the total length of diagram 7287 (stem plus red bar) is 420 mm (see figure 13-7). Where a sign to diagram 7201 is manufactured so that the arrow head can be changed to a red bar, all arrows should have a length of 720 mm whether or not the red bar is displayed. This type of sign is likely to be used where a closed lane is opened to traffic during peak hours. As the sign to diagram 7201.1 does not use the red bar symbol, a flap type variable message sign, with a reduced number of arrows, could be used where a lane is closed for part of the day.

13.18 The length of the white contra-flow arrow (diagram 7288) will normally be 720 mm, including the black edge. Figure 13-8 shows how this arrow is placed alongside an upward pointing arrow.

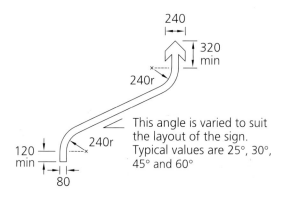

determining the position of the arrows. The vertical edges of the central reservation symbol, red block and hard shoulder line should be treated in the same way as the sign border when using the table. A horizontal bar may be used where two or more unsegregated lanes lead to the same named destination or route (see diagram 7212). The design of this bar is the same as for diagram 7201 (see figure 13-6). The 150 mm radius on the red block is applied only where there is a curved arrow immediately adjacent. Where there is a hard shoulder line between the red block and the arrow, a non-radiused corner is used. A non-radiused corner is also used in diagram 7240, where the bifurcation arrow does not have a fillet (see figure 13-18).

LANE CHANGE ARROW DETAIL

All dimensions are in millimetres

Figure 13-8

DESIGN OF SIGNS SHOWING LANE CHANGES

13.19 Diagrams 7210 to 7218 inclusive show lane changes which occur in contra-flow situations. The central reservation is represented by the solid black symbol and the areas of closed carriageway by red blocks. Where traffic is directed onto a hard shoulder, a thin black line is used to denote the division between the hard shoulder and the normal running lane. Figure 13-9 shows the basic design details for the curved arrows, red blocks, central reservation symbol and hard shoulder demarcation line. The table in figure 13-4 is applicable to these signs when

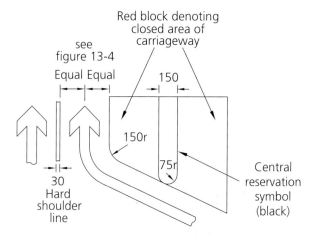

RED BLOCK, CENTRAL RESERVATION and HARD SHOULDER SYMBOL DETAILS

All dimensions are in millimetres

Figure 13-9

13.20 The design of the centre panel is carried out by combining the elements shown in figure 13-9. The design details for combining these elements are shown in figure 13-10. Where there are three or more lanes on the approach to the lane change, the stems at the base of the arrows should, wherever possible, be equally spaced with a minimum dimension of 400 mm centre to centre. The minimum dimension from the centre line of the arrow shaft to any border, central reservation symbol, red block or hard shoulder symbol is 200 mm.

13.21 Diagrams 7230 to 7239 inclusive show lane changes within the same carriageway (i.e. not involving contra-flow). The design principles are the same as those for the contra-flow signs described in paras 13.19 and 13.20 except that the central reservation symbol is not used.

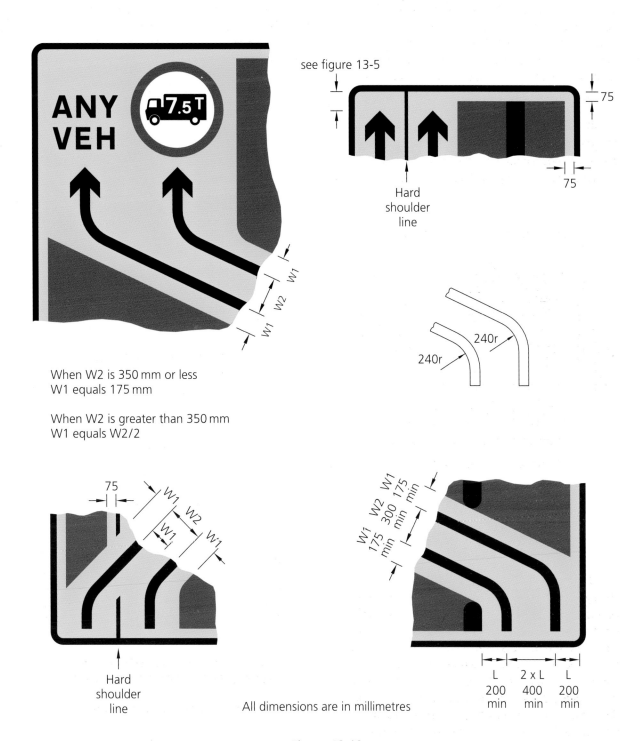

When W2 is 350 mm or less
W1 equals 175 mm

When W2 is greater than 350 mm
W1 equals W2/2

All dimensions are in millimetres

Figure 13-10

13.22 Diagrams 7235 and 7236 are used to indicate the start and end of narrow lanes respectively. The design of the curved arrows is shown in figure 13-11. The examples shown for combining arrows assume that the carriageway restriction is on the left hand side. The arrows are reversed where the restriction is on the right hand side of the carriageway.

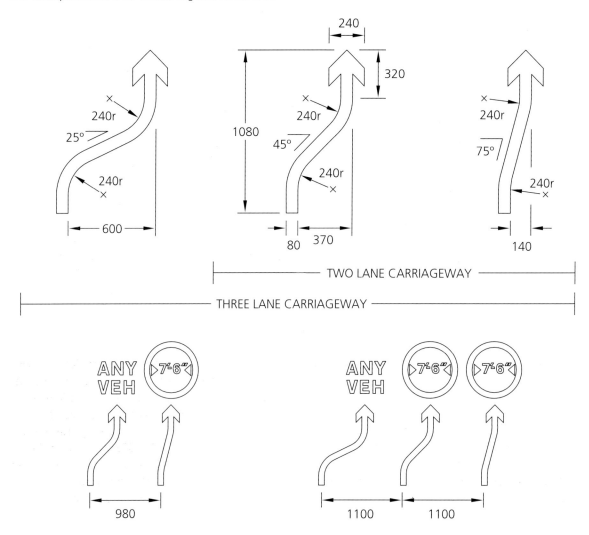

START OF NARROW LANES (TWO and THREE LANE CARRIAGEWAYS)

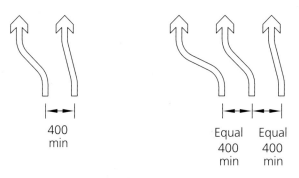

END OF NARROW LANES (TWO and THREE LANE CARRIAGEWAYS)

All dimensions are in millimetres

Figure 13-11

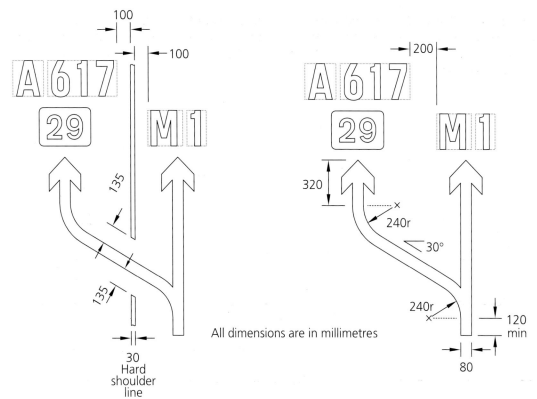

Figure 13-12

13.23 The bifurcation arrow in diagram 7233 is used to indicate that an additional lane has become available. In this case traffic wishing to leave the motorway is directed onto the hard shoulder. This bifurcation arrow is detailed in figure 13-12 and may be used with any other centre panel design (including contra-flow signs) where appropriate. Where traffic is not directed onto the hard shoulder, the design excluding the hard shoulder line is used.

13.24 The bifurcation arrow shown in diagram 7232 is used where traffic on the hard shoulder rejoins the main carriageway and an additional traffic lane is available. The design of this arrow depends on the number of lanes and on whether the sign has a top panel (REJOIN MAIN CARRIAGEWAY). Figure 13-13 shows the basic design of the bifurcation arrow when there is no top panel (i.e. the width of the sign is determined by the number of lanes indicated). The

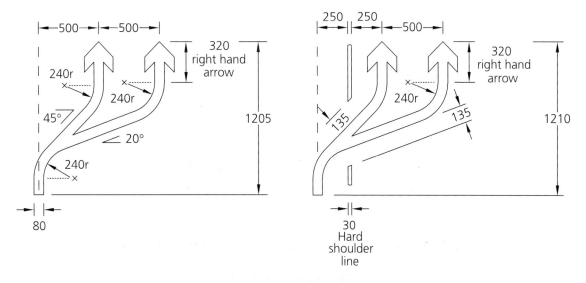

All dimensions are in millimetres

Figure 13-13

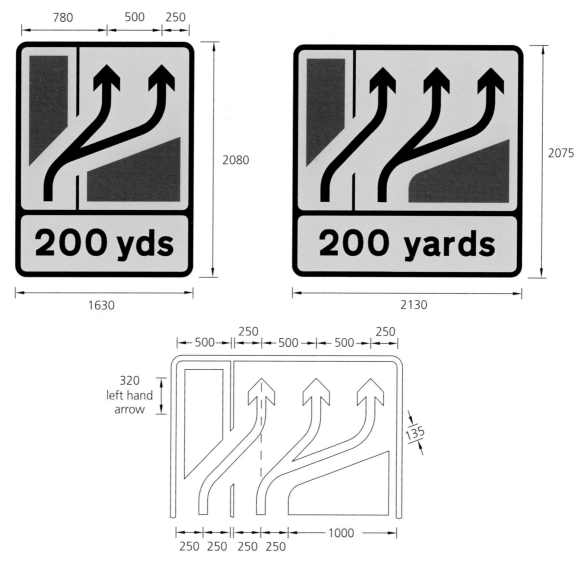

All dimensions are in millimetres

Figure 13-14

arrow design is modified slightly when it crosses the hard shoulder demarcation line. Figure 13-14 shows the layouts of the complete sign for one and two lanes through the works when there is no top panel. In each case only one additional lane is shown beyond the works. It is not necessary to indicate any additional increase in the number of lanes available (e.g. two lanes increasing to four would be shown as two lanes increasing to three). Figures 13-15 and 13-16 show how the arrow design is modified when the sign has a top panel and there are one or two lanes through the works respectively. The overall width of the sign is fixed at 2630 mm irrespective of the number of lanes indicated. Figure 13-17 shows the sign design for three lanes through the works. It should be noted that, in this case, the design of the arrows is the same whether there is a top panel or not.

13.25 Diagram 7231 is used when the number of lanes through the works, using the hard shoulder, remains the same when rejoining the main carriageway. That part of the red block to the right of the right hand arrow head indicates that the third lane of the main carriageway is closed. This sign could be modified by omitting this part of the red block and adjusting the position of the arrows to indicate that the main carriageway is fully open, and has the same number of lanes as through the works (e.g. on a two-lane motorway where lane two is closed and traffic runs on the hard shoulder and lane one).

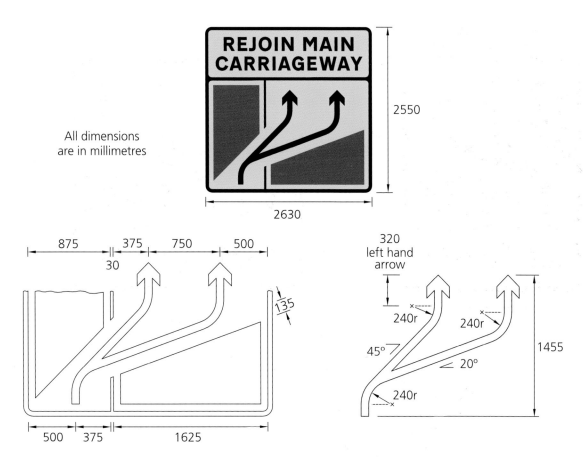

Figure 13-15

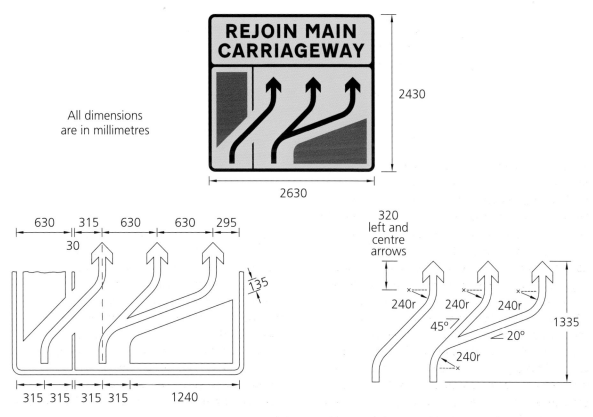

Figure 13-16

13.26 Diagram 7233 does not have a horizontal bar for the two M1 lanes because the route number is repeated for each lane. The bar is used where the destination and/or route number is shown only once.

13.27 Diagrams 7220 and 7240 are used as advance direction signs where access to the junction (usually an exit slip road) is gained through the works area.

Diagram 7220 is used for contra-flow systems where turning traffic crosses the central reserve. Diagram 7240 is used where traffic leaves the main carriageway without crossing the central reservation. The inclined arrow in each case is always angled at 45° upwards to the left. Design details are given in figure 13-18. Details of x-heights are given in figure 13-3 (diagrams 7285 and 7286).

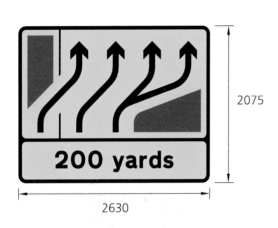

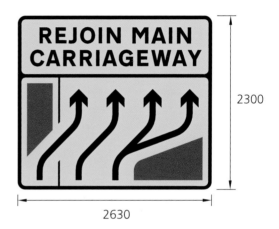

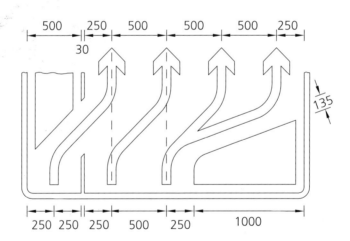

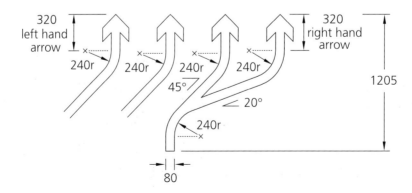

All dimensions are in millimetres

Figure 13-17

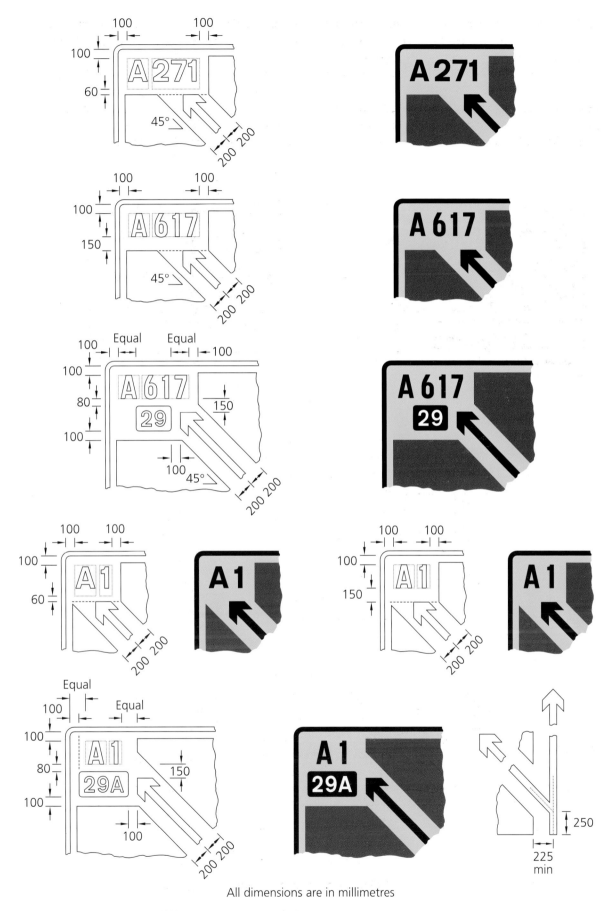

All dimensions are in millimetres

Figure 13-18

13.28 The basic design of diagram 7221 is shown in figure 13-19. The arrows may be varied in accordance with diagrams 7281 to 7286 inclusive (see figure 13-3). The table in figure 13-4 should then be used to obtain the horizontal spacing of the arrows. Wherever possible the approach stems of the arrows should be equally spaced, as shown in figure 13-20.

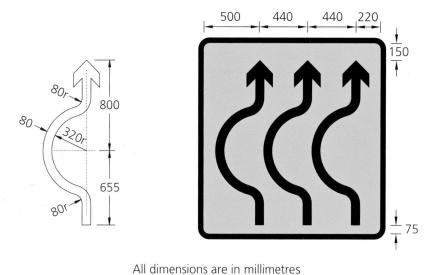

All dimensions are in millimetres

Figure 13-19 (diagram 7221)

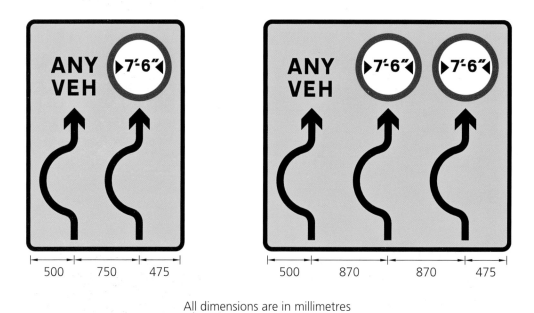

All dimensions are in millimetres

Figure 13-20

GENERAL

14.1 Signs not covered by sections 2 to 13 of this chapter are generally shown in the "P" series of working drawings published by the Stationery Office. These are now being made available on the Department's website. In many cases, the drawings include details of permitted variants. However, where it is necessary to design a sign to suit a particular requirement, the working drawings may not show all the possible variations. This section includes standard design details that should be used for the permitted variants listed against some of the signs in the Regulations.

14.2 Regulation 53 prescribes signs for certain temporary situations. Although the Regulations do not specify the style of lettering, it is strongly recommended that the Transport alphabet is used and that the signs are designed in accordance with the rules set out in this chapter. Lower case legend should generally be used in preference to capitals only, as the former lends itself to easy recognition of words from the shapes created by the ascenders and descenders. Where white letters are used on a red background (regulation 53(6)(d)), it is more appropriate to use capital letters, as in diagrams 7010.1 to 7016. The signs may be either rectangular or flag type (with a chevron). A rectangular sign may

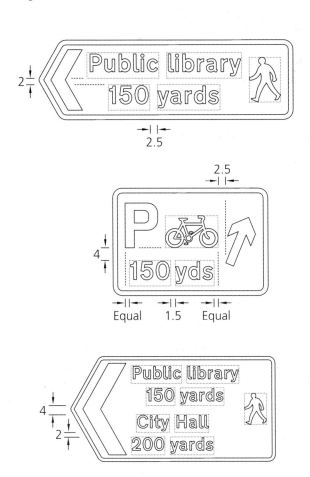

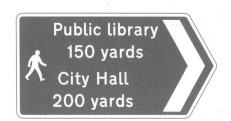

Figure 14-1

include an arrow as used on a stack type sign. Where blue characters are used on a white background (regulation 53(6)(c)), the Transport Heavy alphabet should be used. The Regulations allow for an x-height range of 40 mm minimum to 250 mm (350 mm capital letter) maximum based on the Transport alphabet. The length of arrow prescribed by Regulation 53 is equivalent to an x-height range of 62.5 mm minimum to 250 mm maximum, assuming that the arrow length is 16 sw. The signs may incorporate any symbol prescribed by the Regulations. Signs prescribed by regulation 53 may be used for a maximum period of six months, except that the sign illustrated in figure 11-3 may be used for a period of up to two years. Signs which are to be retained for longer periods will require special authorisation (see direction 38(1)).

DISTANCES

14.3 Appendix G lists those directional signs where a distance may be expressed in the form "x yards", "x yds" or "X YARDS", the latter generally being used only on those signs that have capital letters throughout. The distance should normally be centred horizontally below the destination with a vertical gap, as shown in figure 14-1. It is recommended that only one destination is shown on this type of sign. However, figure 14-1 shows the correct vertical spacing where more than one destination is included.

14.4 Exceptionally, the distance may be placed alongside the destination as shown in figure 14-2. Unless shown otherwise on a working drawing, the distance shall always be to the right of the

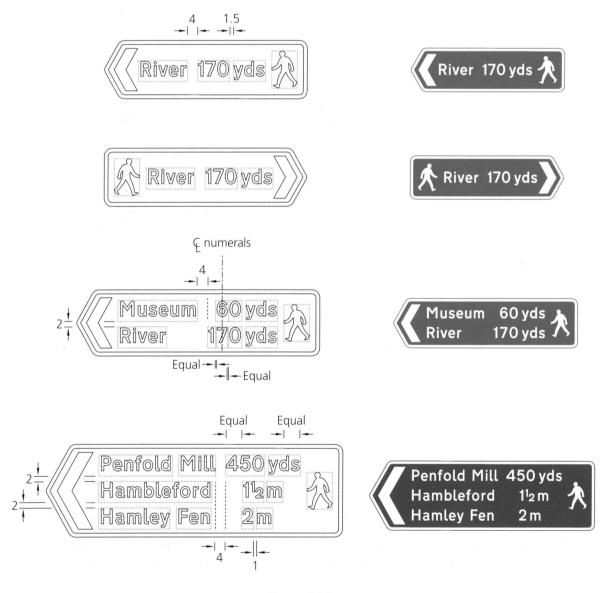

Figure 14-2

destination when placed on the same line. As the units of measurement (e.g. "yds") are included, the horizontal gap between the place name and the distance is reduced from the standard 7 sw to 4 sw. Where two or more destinations are shown on the same sign, the distances are generally aligned in columns as shown in the "Museum - River" example (note that the gap between "1" and "7" is the same as that between "7" and "0" in "170 yds"). Generally, for pedestrian signs, the stacking order of destinations is nearest first. The Regulations require that distances over 1/2 mile should be expressed in miles and not yards. Figure 14-2 includes an example of a sign where distances are expressed in both yards and miles. This is most likely to occur on public footpath signs. The abbreviation "m" is used for miles. The first distance to be shown in miles is centred beneath the distance in yards on the line immediately above. Subsequent distances in miles will have the unit numerals aligned in a column. Thus in the example, the "2" is centred beneath the "1". Where fractions of miles are used with whole miles (as in the example), it is not practicable to position the "m"s in a column. However, where two or more adjacent lines contain either whole miles or fractions (but not a mixture of both), the "m"s on those lines should be aligned in columns, with the smallest gap to an adjacent numeral tile being 1 sw. Where a public footpath sign shows all distances as miles, the "m" is omitted and the minimum horizontal gap to the place name increased to the standard 7 sw.

14.5 Metric distances are not permitted by the Regulations, and must not be used.

ADDING ARROWS BENEATH DESTINATIONS

14.6 The design rules for regulatory signs in respect of horizontal arrows beneath tiled legends also apply to other signs (i.e. the vertical gap is 1.5 sw). Where the arrow is directly below a symbol the vertical gap is 2.5 sw.

LANE GAIN SIGNS

14.7 The number of arrows on the lane gain signs shown in Schedule 4 to the Regulations may be varied to suit the circumstances. This is a straightforward process for the signs on the main carriageway where the arrow heads are vertical. Each

additional arrow (straight or curved) increases the width of the sign by 13 sw, as detailed on the working drawings. However, the signs mounted on the entry slip roads have arrow heads angled at 45°. This complicates the addition or deletion of arrows. Figure 14-3 shows the basic design rules which apply in this case. *The minimum length of any straight arrow is 16 sw.* Other design details (e.g. lane line dimensions) can be found on the working drawings.

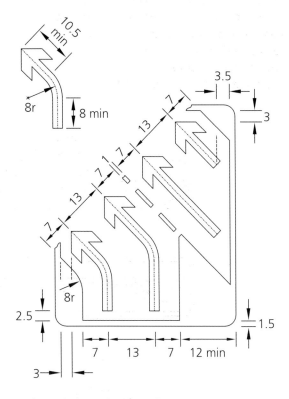

Figure 14-3

14.8 The minimum length of arrow (straight or curved) should be increased where this would improve the appearance of the sign. For example, a very short arrow may be lost on a sign that also contains several long arrows.

14.9 *Lane gain signs must not be modified for use as rectangular lane merge signs.* Triangular warning signs to diagrams 508.1 and 509.1 should be used where traffic merges need to be signed (see Chapter 4). In situations where it is considered that a rectangular sign might be of benefit, special authorisation must be sought (see para 1.10).

All dimensions are in stroke widths
based on the main x-height

Figure 14-4

STACK TYPE SIGNS WITH SUPPLEMENTARY MESSAGES AT REDUCED X-HEIGHT

14.10 Where a supplementary message at 80% of the main x-height is used on a stack type sign, the vertical position of the legend tiles relative to the arrow is determined as shown in figure 14-4. It should be noted that the design takes account of the rules described in para 3.37 and illustrated in figure 3-24. The design rules illustrated in figure 3-9 do not apply in this case.

U-TURN ARROW ON A STACK TYPE SIGN

14.11 Figure 5-33 illustrates the design of a map type sign that includes a destination reached by making a U-turn at a roundabout. This type of sign would generally be used on a dual carriageway where there are no gaps in the central reservation at side road junctions. An alternative to a map type sign is a stack type sign with a U-turn arrow, the design of which is shown in figure 14-5. It should be noted that the arrow is always placed to the right of the legend. The gap between the legend tiles and the arrow is increased from the standard value of 2.5 sw

to 4 sw. This is because the tiles are adjacent to the arrow shaft and not the arrow head. The gap of 4 sw also applies when a symbol, panel or patch is adjacent to the arrow. This sign should indicate the U-turn only. Other directions at the junction should be shown on a separate advance direction sign.

14.12 Any symbol that has a directional element to its design should face to the right when used with a U-turn arrow. The aircraft symbol, which generally points in the same direction as an arrow, should be horizontal and must not point downwards. Symbols should normally be placed on the left hand side of the sign, except for the aircraft symbol, which is generally placed to the right of the airport name. A symbol may also be centred beneath the associated destination where this results in a more efficient layout, taking account of the height of the U-turn arrow. An example is shown in figure 14-5.

14.13 Triangular warning signs and regulatory roundel signs may be included on U-turn signs and should follow the same design rules as for other stack type signs. However, the horizontal gap between the triangle or roundel and the arrow should be increased from 2.5 sw to 4 sw. A U-turn sign may

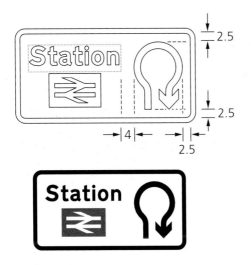

Sign height determined by arrow

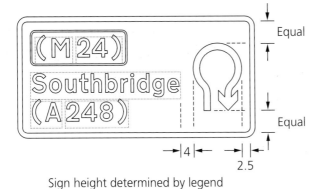

Sign height determined by legend

Figure 14-5

include an alternative route message and should be designed in accordance with figure 14-4.

14.14 As a U-turn sign generally indicates the same road that it is located on, panels indicating a different status of route are not normally used (but see para 14.15). However, the sign may include a bracketed route number patch as shown in figure 14-5.

14.15 There may be certain junction layouts where a U-turn at a roundabout does not lead back to the same route (e.g. an urban one-way system, or a grade separated junction). A map type sign may be more appropriate in this situation, but a separate U-turn sign could be provided if necessary. If the status of the route changes, a panel should be used.

SIZE AND SPACING OF SYMBOLS

14.16 The sizes of symbols when used on directional informatory signs are specified in Appendix B. On certain signs, more than one symbol may be placed

on one line. Alternatively, two symbols, one above the other, may be associated with the same legend. In both these circumstances, the standard sizes for the symbols may produce an out of balance pictorial representation. A good example is the car and lorry symbols, where the car symbol is actually the larger of the two. A similar problem occurs with the lorry and bus symbols, and reference to figure 12-7 (commercial vehicles waiting prohibition plates) shows that it is necessary to modify the sizes. In the case of figure 12-7, the lorry has been increased in size from 24 x 12 sw to 30 x 15 sw, and the bus reduced in size from 40 x 13 sw to 34 x 11.05 sw. The general rule is that where two symbols appear out of balance, one should be increased in size and the other reduced. An example is shown in figure 14-6. To leave one symbol the same size could result in the other symbol (which has either been increased or reduced in size) being out of balance with other elements of the sign and inappropriate for the size of x-height being used.

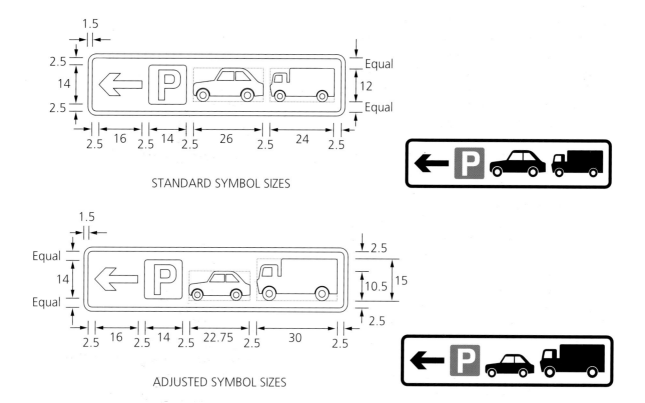

Figure 14-6

14.17 Where signs incorporating more than one symbol on the same line are shown on the working drawings (e.g. diagrams 2603, 2606, 2608 and 2701 variant), the symbol sizes shown should not be changed. Similarly, tourist attraction symbols have fixed sizes which should not be changed.

14.18 The horizontal gap between symbols on the same line is generally 2.5 sw. However, the appearance of the sign can sometimes be improved by increasing this value to 4 sw. There are no fixed rules regarding symbol spacing, except those shown on the working drawings. Where the spacing of particular symbols is not covered by the drawings, designers should use their discretion in deciding whether the horizontal gap should be increased to 4 sw. The aim is to ensure that the symbols on the sign in question are clearly discernible as separate entities when viewed from a distance, and avoid a cluttered appearance.

USE OF BACKING BOARDS

14.19 To improve conspicuity against a complex or dark background, a sign may be mounted on either a grey or a yellow backing board (direction 42(5)). This

board must *not* be provided with an additional black border. White backing boards are not permitted. No legend may be applied directly to a backing board. Under no circumstances must striped or chequered backing boards be used. Not only are these unsightly, but they tend to camouflage the sign by breaking up its outline. They are also unlawful. Where a yellow board is used, this should not have the appearance of an additional sign border. The minimum width of any yellow area on a single rectangular sign should therefore be 6 sw. In the case of the chevron sign shown in diagram 515, the width of the yellow area should not be less than half the horizontal width of the white chevron. Triangular yellow borders and circular backing boards producing a bullseye effect are not permitted (direction 42(6)).

14.20 Yellow backing boards, particularly if they use fluorescent material, can be very effective in drawing attention to signs mounted in deep shadow, for example below overhanging trees.

14.21 There are, however, potential disadvantages to the use of backing boards. A grey board can deprive triangular and circular signs of a primary recognition aid, their distinctive silhouettes. Yellow backing boards can be environmentally intrusive, and their over-use could eventually devalue their attention-attracting benefits. A less garish way of increasing a sign's conspicuity may be simply to provide a standard sign of larger size. Not only will this be more noticeable than a smaller sign, but it will also improve legibility and hence reading distance, which a yellow backing board cannot.

14.22 Grey backing boards can be used to mount an assembly of signs. The minimum space between any sign and the edge of the backing board should be 50 mm. The minimum space between any two signs should be 4 sw, or 100 mm where the signs do not have worded legends (except supplementary plates, see figure 14-8). Where there are more than two signs, the spaces between each of the signs should be equal. Signs of different lengths should be centred horizontally on the backing board. Two flag type signs pointing in opposite directions should normally be mounted side by side, but where site constraints require that one sign should be mounted above the other, the assembly may look more balanced if the shorter sign is positioned slightly off-centre. The various elements of the signs shown in diagrams 2020, 2021, 2021.1, 2114.1, 2116, 2117, 2913.4 and the destination panels in diagrams 2908, 2908.1 and 2909 may have the borders touching, but not overlapping. An example of the use of a grey backing board is shown in figure 14-7. Directional signs should not be mounted on yellow backing boards. This is needlessly visually intrusive, and if increased conspicuity is necessary, this is more usefully achieved by using a larger x-height for the sign.

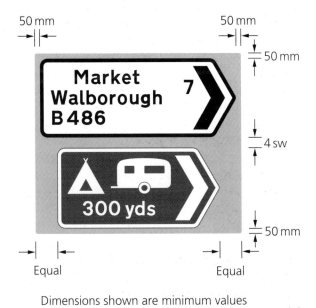

Dimensions shown are minimum values

Figure 14-7

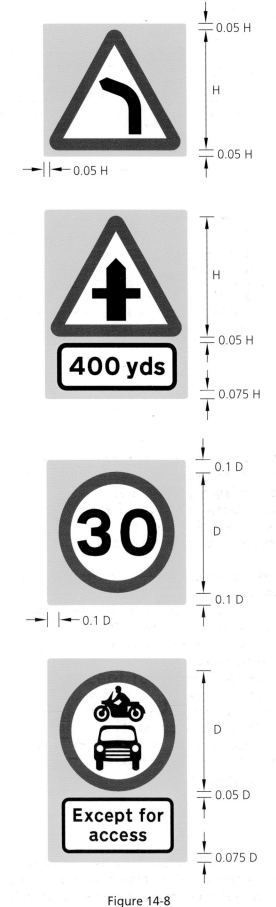

Figure 14-8

14.23 The minimum recommended dimensions for mounting triangular signs and roundels on grey or yellow backing boards are shown in figure 14-8. Where the supplementary plate is wider than the sign, the space between the vertical edge of the plate and the edge of the backing board should match the space below the plate, i.e. 0.075 H or 0.075 D as appropriate. Where the width of the plate is equal to or greater than the minimum width of backing board required for the sign, the backing board can be flush with the plate at the sides and bottom. Where triangular and roundel signs are mounted one above the other, the vertical space between them should equal one sixth of the height or diameter of the larger sign.

14.24 Where a speed limit roundel to diagram 670 or 671 is mounted on a grey or yellow backing board with the speed camera repeater sign to diagram 879, special design rules apply. These are shown in figure 14-9. The smallest prescribed sign to diagram 879 is used with the 300 mm diameter roundel. Larger roundels are mounted with a sign to diagram 879 which is proportionally smaller but within the range of prescribed sizes.

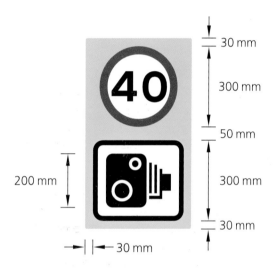

Diameter of speed limit roundel
equal to 300 mm

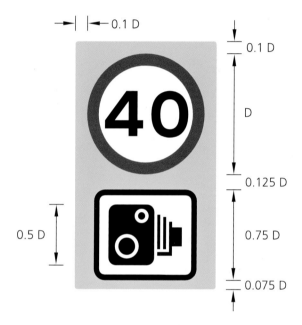

Diameter of speed limit roundel
greater than 300 mm

Figure 14-9

APPENDIX A
Diagrams covered by working drawings

Working drawings under the heading "Working Drawings for Traffic Sign Design and Manufacture" are available in three volumes from the Stationery Office. The reference numbers for each volume are:

Volume 1   ISBN   0-11-551624-7

Volume 2   ISBN   0-11-551627-1

Volume 3   ISBN   0-11-551719-7

These drawings were produced for signs prescribed by the 1994 Regulations and are gradually being replaced by new drawings to take account of the changes introduced by the 2002 Regulations. The new drawings are being made available on the Department's website at "www.dft.gov.uk" together with lists of drawings that are current or have been withdrawn. Diagrams in the 2002 Regulations for which there are working drawings are listed below.

SCHEDULE 1: WARNING SIGNS

Working drawings are issued for all signs in Schedule 1, with the exception of diagrams 528.1, 532.2, 532.3, 560 and 561.

SCHEDULE 2: REGULATORY SIGNS

Working drawings for all signs in Schedule 2 are either issued or in preparation.

SCHEDULE 3: SIGNS FOR RAILWAY AND TRAMWAY LEVEL CROSSINGS

With the exception of diagram 781, working drawings for all signs in Schedule 3 are either issued or in preparation.

SCHEDULE 4: MISCELLANEOUS INFORMATORY SIGNS

Working drawings for all signs in Schedule 4 are either issued or in preparation.

SCHEDULE 5: SIGNS FOR BUS TRAM AND PEDAL CYCLE FACILITIES

With the exception of diagrams 973.2 and 973.3, working drawings for all signs in Schedule 5 are either issued or in preparation.

SCHEDULE 6: ROAD MARKINGS

Working drawings are either issued or being prepared for diagrams 1003.4, 1012.2, 1012.3, 1014, 1027.1 to 1033 inclusive, 1038, 1038.1, 1039, 1050, 1057, 1059 and 1065.

SCHEDULE 7: DIRECTIONAL INFORMATORY SIGNS

Working drawings are either issued or being prepared for the following diagrams. Working drawings for other diagrams may be produced to show sign specific design details not included in this chapter.

2010.1	Route avoiding prohibited movement
2010.2	Route avoiding prohibited movement
2025	Map type sign for by-passed community
2032	Ring road repeater sign
2034	For one destination follow another destination or route
2121	Map type sign for by-passed community
2123	Route avoiding prohibited movement
2124	Route avoiding prohibited movement
2130	Ring road repeater sign
2138	For one destination follow another destination or route
2201	Distance ahead to a tourist attraction
2205	Location of Tourist Information Point or Centre
2208	Symbol only - direction sign
2209	Distance ahead to a tourist attraction
2212	Direction sign indicating a route through places of interest
2215	List of tourist attractions reached from a junction ahead
2217	For one destination follow another destination or route

2301	Distance ahead to camping/caravan site	2512	Direction to a secured car park (flag type sign)
2302	Direction sign indicating camping/caravan site	2513	Map type advance direction sign indicating availability of parking places
2303	Distance ahead to a Youth Hostel		
2304	Direction sign indicating a Youth Hostel	2601.1	Direction of cycle route at junction ahead
2305	Distance ahead to a picnic area	2601.2	Route for pedal cycles at junction ahead
2306	Direction sign indicating a picnic area	2602.1	Direction of cycle route
2307	Distance ahead to a parking place with information and other facilities	2602.2	Cycle route number
		2602.3	Cycle route number (plate)
2308.1	Advance direction sign indicating local facilities	2603	Advance direction sign indicating cycle parking place
2310.1	Sign on a primary or non-primary route indicating an off-line MSA ahead	2604	Direction sign indicating cycle parking place
2313.1	Services ahead on a primary or non-primary route (open 24 hours to all vehicles)	2606	Direction sign indicating a route for pedestrians and cycles
2313.2	Advance direction sign indicating services on primary or non-primary route (open 24 hours to all vehicles)	2607	Special direction sign indicating pedestrian route
		2608	Direction sign indicating pedestrian route to a tourist attraction
2313.3	Services ahead on a primary or non-primary route (not open 24 hours)	2609	Pedestrian route to tourist attraction car park
2313.4	Advance direction sign indicating services on primary or non-primary route (not open 24 hours)	2610	Flag type direction sign indicating public footpath
		2610.1	Rectangular direction sign indicating public footpath
2313.5	Services ahead on a primary or non-primary route (not open to all vehicles)	2610.2	Waymark sign for public footpaths
2313.6	Advance direction sign indicating services on primary or non-primary route (not open to all vehicles)	2701	Direction sign indicating new housing development
2322	Direction sign indicating public telephone	2701.1	Junction ahead leading to new housing development
2323	Direction sign indicating public toilets	2702	Start of temporary diversion route
2328	Junction ahead leading to a by-passed community	2703	Advance direction sign indicating diversion route
2329	Direction to a by-passed community	2704	Direction sign indicating diversion route
2330	No services on motorway	2706	Map type advance direction sign indicating diversion route
2401	County boundary	2708	Route for emergency vehicles to temporary incident control point
2402.1	Name of town/village		
2403.2	Name of town/village plus extra information	2709	Route for emergency vehicles to emergency services incident point
2501	Distance ahead to parking place	2710	Direction sign indicating route for emergency vehicles to emergency services incident point
2502	Distance ahead to parking with additional facilities		
2503	Distance ahead to a "Park and Ride" parking place	2711	Direction to emergency exit for pedestrians from tunnel
2504	Direction sign indicating a "Park and Ride" parking place	2712	Location of fire rendezvous point
		2713	Direction to nearest telephone (motorway marker post)
2506	Direction sign indicating the number of parking places		
2509.1	Variable message advance direction sign indicating availability of parking places	2713.1	Distance ahead to emergency telephone in a parking place
2511	Direction to secured car park (rectangular sign)	2714	Side of emergency telephone box

2715	Back of emergency telephone box
2716	Road ahead closed - follow alternative route
2717	Primary route marker post
2805	Advance direction sign indicating lorry route
2806	Direction sign indicating lorry route
2806.1	For one destination follow another destination or route
2901	Start of motorway regulations
2910	Rectangular direction sign located on nose of exit slip road
2910.1	Rectangular direction sign located on nose of exit slip road
2911	Route confirmatory sign
2912	Junction ahead with another motorway
2915	For one destination follow another destination or route
2917	1 mile advance sign for service area
2918	Distance to next service area
2918.1	No services on motorway
2919.1	1/2 mile advance sign for service area
2920.1	Final advance sign for service area
2922	Entrance to works unit
2927	List of tourist attractions reached from a junction ahead
2927.1	For tourist destination follow another destination or route
2928	County boundary
2929	Advance direction sign indicating lorry route
2929.1	For lorry route destination follow another destination or route
2930	Distance to end of motorway
2931	End of motorway
2932	End of motorway regulations
2933	Keep apart 2 chevrons
2934	Check your distance

SCHEDULE 8: LIGHT SIGNALS FOR CONTROL OF VEHICULAR TRAFFIC

Working drawings either issued or in preparation for diagrams 3001.2 and 3014 only.

SCHEDULE 9: LIGHT SIGNALS FOR PEDESTRIAN AND ANIMAL CROSSINGS

Working drawings either issued or in preparation for diagrams 4002.1, 4003 and 4006. Drawings may also be produced for diagrams 4003.1 to 4003.7 inclusive.

SCHEDULE 10: LANE CONTROL SIGNALS AND SIGNS

Working drawings for all signs issued.

SCHEDULE 11: MATRIX SIGNS AND LIGHT SIGNALS

No drawings are to be provided for this schedule.

SCHEDULE 12: SIGNS ASSOCIATED WITH ROAD WORKS

Working drawings either issued or in preparation for all signs in Schedule 12, with the exception of diagrams 7101.1, 7102, 7103, 7201, 7201.1, 7210 to 7240 inclusive and 7260 to 7288 inclusive.

APPENDIX B
Symbols used on directional informatory signs

GENERAL SYMBOLS

Working Drawing No.	Description	Size in stroke widths (see section 14)		Directional	Notes
		Width	Height		
S 2	Walking figure	10	14	YES	
S 16	Car (side view)	26	12	YES	Parking signs only
S 17	Car & caravan	35	14	YES	Parking signs only
S 23	Solo motor cycle	18	12	YES	Parking signs only
S 24	Bicycle	17	10	YES	
S 25	Bus	40	13	YES	1. Parking signs only 2. Door replaced by window when facing right
S 30	Aircraft	10	10	YES	1. Size applies when horizontal or vertical 2. Generally faces same direction as route symbol, arrow or chevron, but never downwards
S 32	Lorry	24	12	YES	
S 34	Ferry	46	12	YES	
S 38	Railway station	16	10		0.5 sw white border added when placed on a dark background
S 39	London Underground Station	12.5	10		White tile 14 x 11 sw used when placed on a dark background
S 41	Telephone (Tile A)	14	20	YES	Inclined at 60 degrees
S 43	Parking place	14 (20)	14 (20)		Size relates to "P" symbol on blue patch. Bracketed size is for use on limited waiting signs (see section 12). When placed directly on a blue background the size of the "P" is 12 x 16 sw. The working drawing also gives details of the "Secured" panel
S 44	Public toilets	14	14		
S 45	Disabled persons	14	14	YES	The black tile is omitted and the symbol size is 12 x 14 sw when placed directly on a dark background. Symbol on blue tile is not to be used on directional signs

GENERAL SYMBOLS (Cont'd)

Working Drawing No.	Description	Size in stroke widths (see section 14)		Directional	Notes
		Width	Height		
S 48	Shopmobility	14	14	YES	The black tile is omitted and the symbol size is 15 x 14 sw when placed directly on a dark background
S 49	Hospital	14	14		See working drawing for sizes of "A & E" and "Minor injury unit" plates
S 53	Domestic house	14	14		
S 54	Vehicle testing station	16.1	14		
S 55	Motorway	18	16		
S 56	Diversion route - Square	7.5	7.5		Size of yellow patch
S 56	Diversion route - Triangle	8.5	7.5		Size of yellow patch
S 56	Diversion route - Circle	7.5	7.5		Size of yellow patch
S 56	Diversion route - Diamond	11.5	7.5		Size of yellow patch
S 59	Recycling centre	12.5	12		Grid size (symbol does not fill grid). White tile 14 x 14 sw used when placed on a dark background

TOURIST ATTRACTIONS OR FACILITIES

Working Drawing No.	Description	Size in Stroke Widths		Directional	Notes
		Width	Height		
T 1	Tourist Information Point	14	14		
T 2	Castle	15	14		
T 3	Historic house	13	14		
T 4	Picnic area	14	14		
T 5	Youth Hostel	21	14		
T 6	Caravan site	24	14		
T 7	Camping site	15	14		
T 8	Woodland recreation area	16	14		
T 9	Viewpoint	7	14	YES	
T 10	Light refreshment facilities	10	7.25		
T 11	Restaurant	8	12		

TOURIST ATTRACTIONS OR FACILITIES (Cont'd)

Working Drawing No.	Description	Size in stroke widths		Directional	Notes
		Width	Height		
T 12	Hotel or other overnight accommodation	26	14	YES	
T 101	National Trust property	14	14		
T 102	Flower garden	9	14	YES	
T 103	Preserved railway	18	12	YES	
T 104	Water sports activities	14	14	YES	
T 105	Church	13	14		
T 106	Cathedral	13	14		
T 107	Wildlife park	14	14		
T 108	Windmill	12	14		
T 109	Zoo	17	12	YES	
T 110	Agricultural museum	24	12	YES	
T 111	Equestrian centre	14	14		
T 112	Country park	16	13		
T 113	Bird garden	8	14	YES	
T 114	Pleasure or theme park	24	14		1. Width reduced to 18 sw when only one tree 2. Width reduced to 12 sw when no trees
T 115	Nature reserve	17	11	YES	
T 116	Historic dockyard	14	14	YES	
T 117	Air museum	16	14		
T 118	Beach	13	14		
T 119	Farm park	16	12	YES	
T 120	Pottery or craft centre	10	14		
T 121	Prehistoric site or monument	11	14		
T 122	Butterfly farm	17	11		
T 123	Canal-side attraction	32	8	YES	
T 124	Industrial heritage	14	14		
T 125	Watermill	14	14		
T 126	Aquarium or oceanarium	14	11	YES	
T 127	Site with Roman remains	14	14	YES	
T 128	Heavy horse centre	15	12	YES	

TOURIST ATTRACTIONS OR FACILITIES (Cont'd)

Working Drawing No.	Description	Size in stroke widths		Directional	Notes
		Width	Height		
T 129	Motor museum	20	11	YES	
T 130	Craft centre or forge	16	9	YES	
T 131	Spa, spring or fountain	8	14		
T 132	Farm trail	12	14		
T 133	Vineyard	11	15		
T 134	Golf course	13	14	YES	
T 135	Race course	18	14	YES	
T 136	Motor sport	11	14		
T 137	Cricket ground	12	14		
T 138	Football ground	14	14		
T 139	Canoeing	18	14	YES	
T 140	Fishing	14	14	YES	
T 141	Boat hire	26	11	YES	
T 142	Cycle hire	14	13	YES	
T 143	Woodland walk in a coniferous forest	14	14	YES	
T 144	Woodland walk in a deciduous or mixed forest	16	14	YES	
T 145	Outdoor pursuits centre	12	14	YES	
T 146	Roller skating	14	14	YES	
T 147	Ice skating	14	14	YES	
T 148	Ski slope	14	14	YES	
T 149	Ten pin bowling	12	14		
T 150	Birds of prey centre	22	14	YES	
T 151	RSPB bird reserve	14	14		
T 152	Centre approved by the Rare Breeds Survival Trust	14	11		
T 153	Safari park	23	11	YES	
T 154	Battlefield site	14	10		
T 155	Brass rubbing centre	12	14		
T 156	Tower or folly	10	14		
T 157	Historic building	11	14		
T 158	Lighthouse open to the public	14	16		

TOURIST ATTRACTIONS OR FACILITIES (Cont'd)

Working Drawing No.	Description	Size in stroke widths		Directional	Notes
		Width	Height		
T 159	Pier	24	14	YES	
T 160	Swimming pool or indoor water sports centre	14	14	YES	
T 161	Tram museum	25	14	YES	
T 162	Bus museum	22	12	YES	
T 163	Cinema	20	12	YES	
T 164	Theatre or concert hall	12	14		
T 201	English Tourist Board	14	14		Grid size (symbol does not fill grid)
T 202	English Heritage	14	14		
T 203	Museum or art gallery (England)	16	14		
T 204	Sports centre (England)	14	14		
T 205	National Nature Reserve designated by English Nature	14	14		
T 301.1	Tourist attraction recognised by VisitScotland	12	16		
T 302	Historic property (Scotland)	14	14		
T 303	National Trust for Scotland	12	14		Size applies to white tile
T 304	Forestry Commission property (Scotland)	19	16		Size applies to white tile
T 401	Wales Tourist Board	21	14		Size applies to white tile
T 402	Museum or art gallery (Wales)	16	14		
T 403	Cadw property (Wales)	14	14		Size applies to white tile

APPROVED SYMBOLS FOR TOURIST ATTRACTIONS OR FACILITIES

The Regulations, in Schedule 16, items 24 and 33, make reference to "approved symbols". These are symbols which from time to time are introduced by the Department and can be used without special authorisation. Where a non-prescribed symbol is authorised for a specific attraction it does not necessarily become an approved symbol. Those symbols that are approved will be shown on working drawings prefixed by "AT" and made available on the Department's website. It is intended that approved symbols will be added to Schedule 14 when the Regulations are revised.

APPENDIX C
Width of alphabet tiles

NOTE: The National Assembly for Wales can provide details of special characters used on bilingual signs.

Table 1: Tile widths for Transport Medium alphabet

The widths are given in stroke widths ($\frac{1}{4}$ of the x-height)

Upper case		Lower case		Numerals		Punctuation marks etc		
A	5.44	a	4.44	1	3.16	&	5.04	
B	5.88	b	4.68	2	4.80	(	4.20	
C	5.92	c	4.12	3	5.08	)	4.20	
D	6.16	d	4.76	4	5.28	?	5.52	
E	5.28	e	4.36	5	4.88	.	2.12	full stop
F	4.76	f	3.00	6	5.04	·	2.12	raised point
G	6.20	g	4.56	7	4.16	:	2.12	colon
H	6.40	h	4.48	8	5.20	,	2.60	comma
I	2.92	i	2.16	9	5.12	'	1.56	apostrophe
J	3.72	j	2.32	0	5.32	-	2.64	hyphen
K	5.52	k	4.32			'-	3.40	feet
L	4.28	l	2.48	$\frac{1}{4}$	4.92	"	3.68	inches
M	7.36	m	6.56	$\frac{1}{2}$	5.28	/	3.12	(lower case)
N	6.72	n	4.48	$\frac{3}{4}$	5.92	/	3.12	(upper case)
O	6.24	o	4.72	$\frac{1}{3}$	5.16	£	5.36	
P	5.20	p	4.72	$\frac{2}{3}$	6.60	%	6.40	
Q	6.32	q	4.72					
R	5.64	r	3.20					
S	5.48	s	3.88	UPPER CASE widths when followed by				
T	4.36	t	3.24	lower case a, e, g, o, r, or u :-				
U	6.16	u	4.60					
V	5.20	v	3.92	T 3.92; V 4.52; Y 4.44				
W	7.32	w	5.88					
X	5.12	x	4.16					
Y	4.92	y	3.92	UPPER CASE W is 7.56 wide when				
Z	4.76	z	3.88	followed by upper case T, V, X, Y or Z				

Table 2: Tile widths for White Motorway characters (permanent signs)

The widths are given in stroke widths ($\frac{1}{4}$ of the x-height)

Letters		Numerals		Compass points		Punctuation marks etc		
A	7.00	1	4.40	(N)	13.28	&	6.20	
B	6.40	2	6.00	(S)	12.20	(	3.40	
E	5.80	3	6.00	(E)	12.04	)	3.40	
M	8.00	4	6.60	(W)	14.12	/	4.40	
		5	6.00	(NE)	18.56	,	2.50	comma
		6	6.00	(SE)	17.52			
		7	5.60	(NW)	20.48			
		8	6.00	(SW)	19.44			
		9	6.00					
		0	6.00					

Table 3: Tile widths for Transport Heavy alphabet

The widths are given in stroke widths ($\frac{1}{4}$ of the x-height)

Upper case		Lower case		Numerals		Punctuation marks etc		
A	5.68	a	4.44	1	3.36	&	5.08	
B	5.84	b	4.48	2	5.00	(	4.60	
C	6.04	c	4.28	3	5.44	)	4.60	
D	6.00	d	4.76	4	5.52	?	5.80	
E	5.44	e	4.40	5	5.20	.	2.24	full stop
F	4.84	f	3.16	6	5.16	·	2.24	raised point
G	6.24	g	4.68	7	4.28	:	2.24	colon
H	6.36	h	4.76	8	5.52	,	2.72	comma
I	2.92	i	2.20	9	5.16	'	1.64	apostrophe
J	3.80	j	2.84	0	5.80	-	2.84	hyphen
K	5.52	k	4.56			'-	3.52	feet
L	4.72	l	2.52	$\frac{1}{4}$	5.20	"	4.04	inches
M	7.44	m	6.92	$\frac{1}{2}$	5.44	/	3.24	(lower case)
N	6.72	n	4.76	$\frac{3}{4}$	6.48	/	3.24	(upper case)
O	6.32	o	4.60	$\frac{1}{3}$	5.44	£	5.60	
P	5.36	p	4.80	$\frac{2}{3}$	6.88	%	6.40	
Q	6.44	q	4.80					
R	5.92	r	3.40					
S	5.84	s	4.00					
T	4.72	t	3.36					
U	6.28	u	4.80					
V	5.32	v	4.28					
W	7.72	w	6.40					
X	5.20	x	4.40					
Y	5.12	y	4.24					
Z	4.76	z	3.72					

UPPER CASE widths when followed by lower case a, e, g, o, r, or u :-

T 4.24; V 4.80; Y 4.72

UPPER CASE W is 8.00 wide when followed by upper case T, V, X, Y or Z

Table 4: Tile widths for Black Motorway characters (temporary signs)

The widths are given in stroke widths ($\frac{1}{4}$ of the x-height)

Letters		Numerals		Compass points		Punctuation marks etc		
A	7.36	1	4.60	(N)	13.80	&	6.40	
B	6.48	2	6.24	(S)	12.60	(	3.40	
E	6.00	3	6.24	(E)	13.02	)	3.40	
M	8.24	4	6.64	(W)	15.08	/	4.48	
		5	6.24	(NE)	19.62	,	2.50	comma
		6	6.24	(SE)	18.54			
		7	5.68	(NW)	21.57			
		8	6.24	(SW)	20.50			
		9	6.24					
		0	6.24					

APPENDIX D
Triangle and roundel sizes on directional signs

Diagram No.	Description	Height in sw
523.1	Downhill gradient	24
524.1	Uphill gradient	24
528	Hump bridge	20
529	Swing bridge	20
529.1	Tunnel	20
530	Headroom	24
544	Zebra crossing	20
552	Cattle grid	30
554	"Ford", "Gate" or "Gates"	24
555.1	Water course alongside road	20
557.1	Road hump	20
612	No right turn	16
613	No left turn	16
616	No entry	16
617 with 618.1	Vehicles prohibited	16
619	Motor vehicles prohibited (motorcycle symbol may be reversed)	20
619.1	Motor vehicles other than motorcycles prohibited	20
619.2	Motorcycles prohibited (symbol may be reversed)	20
622.1A	Heavy goods vehicles prohibited (symbol may be reversed)	30
622.5	Horse drawn vehicles prohibited (symbol may be reversed)	20
622.7	Towed caravans prohibited (symbol may be reversed)	20
622.8	Vehicles carrying explosives prohibited	24
626.2A	Weak bridge (roundel only)	24
629	Width restriction (imperial)	24
629A	Width restriction (combined imperial & metric)	30
629.1	Length restriction (imperial) (symbol may be reversed)	30
629.2	Height restriction (imperial)	24
629.2A	Height restriction (combined imperial & metric)	30
770	Level crossing with gate or barrier	20
771	Level crossing without gate or barrier	20
772	Tram crossing	20
779	Electrified cable	20
950	Cycle route warning sign	20
952	Buses prohibited (symbol may be reversed)	20
953 with 953.2	Buses and cycles only (symbols may be reversed)	20
953.1 with 953.2	Trams only	20

NOTES

1. Where two signs of different sizes are placed side by side, the larger size should be used for both.

2. Supplementary plates have an x-height of 80% of the main x-height.

APPENDIX E
Diagrams covered by section 12

Diag. No.	Description	Diag. No.	Description
618	Play Street	660.3	Parking for permit holders
618.1	No vehicles	660.4	Loading only
618.2	Pedestrian zone	660.5	Voucher parking
618.3	Pedestrian zone	660.6	Shared use parking place
618.3A	Pedestrian zone	660.7	Shared use parking place
620	Except for access	661A	Parking for disabled badge holders
620.1	Except for loading	661.1	Limited waiting
636.2	Temporary no stopping	661.2A	Pay at machine
637.2	No waiting (pedestrian zone)	661.3A	Pay here at machine
637.3	No waiting at any time (part year)	662	Disc zone
638.1	No loading	663	Controlled zone
639	No waiting	663.1	Voucher parking zone
639.1B	Various waiting restrictions	665	Goods vehicle "no waiting" zone
640	No waiting and no loading	667.1	Partial verge/footway parking
640.2A	No waiting by goods vehicles	668.1	Full verge/footway parking
640.3	Loading area	961	Time plate for bus or cycle lane
640.4	No waiting in loading area	962	Bus lane at junction ahead
642.2A	No stopping at school entrance	962.1	Cycle lane at junction ahead
646	Urban clearway	962.2	Bus and cycle lane at junction ahead
650.1	No stopping except taxis	972	Photostop for buses
650.2	No waiting except taxis	974	No stopping except buses
650.3	No waiting with taxi exemption	975	Bus stand
660	Parking for permit holders		

NOTES

1. Diagrams 637.1 (no waiting on verge or footway) and 638 (no loading at any time) have fixed designs which are shown on the respective working drawings.

2. Diagram 972 is not a regulatory sign, but does include times of operation.

3. Reference to the "P" series of working drawings should also be made when designing the above signs.

APPENDIX F
Diagrams covered by section 13

7201

7201.1

7210

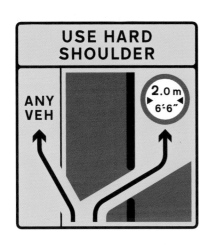

7211.1

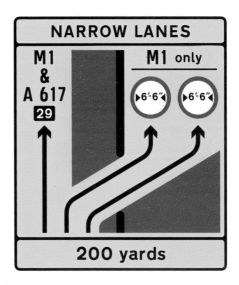

7212

7213

7214

7215

7216

7217

7218

7220

7221

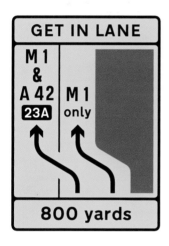

7230

7231

7232

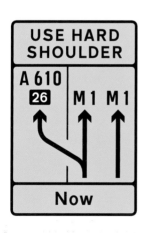

7233

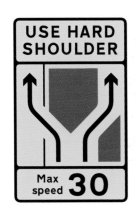

7234

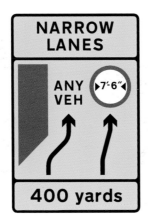

7235

7236

7237

7238

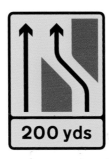

7239

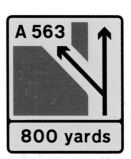

7240

USE HARD SHOULDER

7260

REJOIN MAIN CARRIAGEWAY

7261

GET IN LANE

7262

STAY IN LANE

7263

NARROW LANES

7264

1 mile

7270

200 yards

7271

Now

7272

Narrow lanes

7274

Max speed 30

7275

APPENDIX G
Directional signs where distances may be expressed in yards

2133	Advance direction sign indicating railway station
2134	Direction sign indicating railway station
2135	Advance direction sign indicating a ferry
2136	Direction sign indicating a ferry
2139	Advance direction sign indicating a recycling centre
2140	Direction sign indicating a recycling centre
2201 *	Distance ahead to a tourist attraction
2202	Advance direction sign indicating a tourist attraction
2203	Direction sign indicating a tourist attraction
2204	Direction sign indicating a Tourist Information Point
2205 *	Distance ahead to a Tourist Information Point (see working drawing for special rules)
2216	Stack type advance direction sign indicating tourist attractions along different routes
2301 *	Distance ahead to a camping and caravan site
2302 *	Direction sign indicating a camping and caravan site
2303 *	Distance ahead to Youth Hostel
2304 *	Direction sign indicating a Youth Hostel
2305 *	Distance ahead to a picnic site
2306 *	Direction sign indicating a picnic site
2307 *	Distance ahead to a parking place with a Tourist Information Point
2322 *	Direction sign indicating a payphone
2323 *	Direction sign indicating public toilets
2324	Advance direction sign indicating serviced accommodation
2325	Direction sign indicating serviced accommodation
2326	Advance direction sign indicating refreshment facilities
2327	Direction sign indicating refreshment facilities
2501 *	Distance ahead to a parking place
2502 *	Distance ahead to a commercial vehicles parking place
2503 *	Distance ahead to a "Park and Ride" facility
2504 *	Direction sign indicating a "Park and Ride" facility
2505	Stack type advance direction sign indicating parking places along different routes
2505.1	Stack type advance direction sign indicating parking places along different routes
2506 *	Rectangular direction sign indicating a parking place
2507	Flag type direction sign indicating a parking place
2508	Flag type direction sign indicating a parking place
2509.1 *	Stack type advance direction sign indicating parking places along different routes (VMS)
2510	Direction to a parking place via a U-turn at a roundabout ahead
2511 *	Stack type advance direction sign indicating a secure parking place
2512 *	Flag type direction sign indicating a secure parking place
2513 *	Map type advance direction sign indicating parking places along different routes
2603 *	Advance direction sign indicating a parking place for pedal cycles

2604 *	Direction sign indicating a parking place for pedal cycles
2605	Direction sign indicating a route for pedestrians
2606 *	Direction sign indicating a route for pedestrians and pedal cycles
2607 *	Direction sign indicating a route for pedestrians
2608 *	Direction sign indicating a route for pedestrians to a tourist attraction
2609 *	Direction sign indicating a route for pedestrians to a tourist attraction car park
2610 *	Direction sign indicating a public footpath
2610.1 *	Direction sign indicating a public footpath
2701 *	Direction sign indicating a route to a new housing development
2701.1 *	Advance direction sign indicating a route to a new housing development
2713.1 *	Distance ahead to an emergency telephone
2801	Advance direction sign indicating a Goods Vehicle Testing Station
2802	Direction sign indicating a Goods Vehicle Testing Station

NOTE: The signs marked * have working drawings available or in preparation (see Appendix A).

INDEX

Printed in the United Kingdom for TSO 155512 C15 12/03